PRENTICE-HALL

FOUNDATIONS OF DEVELOPMENTAL BIOLOGY SERIES

Clement L. Markert, Editor

Volumes published or in preparation:

FERTILIZATION   *C. R. Austin*

CONTROL MECHANISMS IN PLANT DEVELOPMENT
Arthur W. Galston and Peter J. Davies

PRINCIPLES OF MAMMALIAN AGING
Robert R. Kohn

EMBRYONIC DIFFERENTIATION
H. E. Lehman

DEVELOPMENTAL GENETICS *   *Clement L. Markert and
Heinrich Ursprung*

CELL REPRODUCTION DURING DEVELOPMENT
David M. Prescott

PATTERNS IN PLANT DEVELOPMENT   *T. A. Steeves and
I. M. Sussex*

CELLS INTO ORGANS: The Forces That Shape
the Embryo   *J. P. Trinkaus*

* Published jointly in Prentice-Hall's *Foundations of Modern Genetics
Series*

PRINCIPLES
OF
MAMMALIAN
AGING

Robert R. Kohn

School of Medicine
Case Western Reserve University

PRENTICE-HALL, INC. Englewood Cliffs, New Jersey

FOUNDATIONS OF DEVELOPMENTAL BIOLOGY SERIES

Printed in the United States of America
C—13-709444-2
P—13-709436-1
Library of Congress Catalog Card Number: 78-152446

Current printing (last digit):

10   9   8   7   6   5   4   3   2   1

PRENTICE-HALL INTERNATIONAL, INC., *London*
PRENTICE-HALL OF AUSTRALIA, PTY. LTD., *Sydney*
PRENTICE-HALL OF CANADA, LTD., *Toronto*
PRENTICE-HALL OF INDIA PRIVATE LIMITED, *New Delhi*
PRENTICE-HALL OF JAPAN, INC., *Tokyo*

For Willy

Foundations of DEVELOPMENTAL BIOLOGY

The development of organisms is so wondrous and yet so common that it has compelled man's attention and aroused his curiosity from earliest times. But developmental processes have proved to be complex and difficult to understand, and little progress was made for hundreds of years. By the beginning of this century, increasingly skillful experimentation began to accelerate the slow advance in our understanding of development. Most important in recent years has been the rapid progress in the related disciplines of biochemistry and genetics— progress that has now made possible an experimental attack on developmental problems at the molecular level. Many old and intractable problems are taking on a fresh appeal, and a tense expectancy pervades the biological community. Rapid advances are surely imminent.

New insights into the structure and function of cells are moving the principal problems of developmental biology into the center of scientific attention, and increasing numbers of biologists are focusing their research efforts on these problems. Moreover, new tools and experimental designs are now available to help in their solution.

At this critical stage of scientific development a fresh assessment is needed. This series of books in developmental biology is designed to provide essential background material and then to examine the frontier where significant advances are occurring or expected. Each book is written by a leading investigator actively concerned with the problems and concepts he discusses. Students at intermediate and advanced levels of preparation and investigators in other areas of biology should find these books informative, stimulating, and useful. Collectively, they present an authoritative and penetrating analysis of the major problems and concepts of developmental biology, together with a critical appraisal of the experimental tools and designs that make developmental biology so exciting and challenging today.

CLEMENT L. MARKERT

Preface

The writing of this book grew out of lectures given to medical students and the preparation of several review articles. These activities and research in the field for around 15 years have compelled me to organize my thinking about aging, particularly about interrelationships of processes at different levels of organization, and cause-and-effect sequences. The big problem has often been in deciding on the most significant questions, and in trying to pose them in specific enough terms for one to know where to look for answers.

It can be quite unsettling to have finished a book on a large, complex, and controversial subject. The anxiety is heightened if the subject is an important one, and it makes a difference if what has been said is true or not. One wonders if there is not, lurking somewhere in the literature, a report that renders untenable some major point in the book. It can be assumed that certain recent papers will make various phenomena and interpretations in the book not exactly as described, and indicate a number of omissions.

If one is presumptuous enough to think he has something to teach, and desires to put it in black-and-white, then perhaps he should be prepared to be wrong and be judged for it. I can take some refuge in the knowledge that scientific conclusions are always tentative and that aging is an important and timely subject, badly in need of a conceptual framework within which theories can be argued and tested. I would be satisfied with a passing grade for effort and intention.

Cleveland, Ohio   ROBERT R. KOHN
April, 1969

Contents

Introduction

The deterioration of objects, animals, and people with the passage of time is a conspicuous feature of the world around us. It seems so natural and commonplace that man, as curious as he is, has until quite recently seldom asked why this should be. As more has been learned about the not-so-visible world of molecules, cells, and tissues, we have found that some type of deterioration also occurs with the passage of time in these systems. Again, these changes have appeared to many as not only commonplace and uninteresting but also somewhat depressing. More enthusiasm can be generated for finding out how systems become better, or how some whimsical phenomenon might be explained, than for trying to understand why something goes to pieces, as it were. In biology, in particular, a hidden idealism stimulates our interest in programming and control mechanisms that make systems more highly developed, more efficient, and capable of maintaining steady states or equilibria.

Scientists appear to possess a collective consciousness or awareness that causes large numbers of them to ask the same type of questions and work toward the same goals during a given period. They also possess collective blind spots that cause them passively to observe phenomena without realizing that some important and challenging questions might be in order. We can imagine the early biologist who reflects momentarily on heredity. He might not consider it exciting that dogs invariably give birth to puppies, and cats have kittens. In order for this observation to be exciting, and to cause one to ask questions, enough basic information and techniques must be available to enable the scientist to advance hypotheses and perform experiments.

The enormous amount of information that has been accumulated on the basic chemistry and structure of living systems has made the era of

1

modern genetics possible. This basic information has also enabled us to formulate hypotheses and carry out experiments aimed toward understanding aging processes at a variety of levels.

In addition to our acquisition of information and techniques necessary for the study of aging processes, we have become aware of the facts that these processes are widespread in nature and constitute exceedingly important theoretical and practical problems. It is difficult to conceive of any population that does not age. Progressive alteration occurs in the nonliving world in populations of molecules, substances, and objects of all kinds. In living systems we can observe progressive changes in populations of molecules in cells and tissues, and, at higher levels of complexity, in organelles and the cells themselves. Many of these processes appear essential for normal development and function. Finally, we can recognize aging processes at the level of the intact organism, where they frequently result in debility, and the end point of death. The notion that all human beings die when they get very old is scarcely new. However, during the eras of famines and epidemics, the main concern was to get through youth and middle age. In modern societies where this is assured for most of the people, the population faces death due to the complications of aging—the 100 percent fatal disease that everyone has. The increased awareness of the role of age in disease, debility, and death has, very appropriately, stimulated interest in the mechanisms of aging processes.

Although questions about aging have only recently begun to interest large numbers of scientists, there is a rich literature on aging which goes back to antiquity. Concepts of aging through history reflect the development of biology and scientific medicine. The earliest concerns were with social and psychological aspects of growing old. Aristotle, in observing the aged, noted, "They lack confidence in the future; partly through experience—for most things go wrong, or anyhow turn out worse than one expects." He also observed and commented on the definite life spans of various organisms. We are indebted to Aristotle for an important hypothesis of aging, perhaps representing the point of view that makes science possible—"The incapacity of old age is due to an affection not of the soul but of its vehicle, as occurs in drunkenness or disease."

Careful observation was characteristic of the Renaissance. Leonardo Da Vinci dissected 30 bodies, and was particularly interested in anatomic changes with age, instructing his students on how various parts of the body should be drawn in the progression of subjects from infancy into old age. He paid special attention to connective tissues and blood vessels, and concluded that the cause of aging was "Veins which by the thickening of their tunics in the old restrict the passage of the blood, and by this lack of nourishment destroy the life of the aged without any fever, the old coming to fail little by little in slow death."

Sir Francis Bacon was also a student of aging, and compiled differences between youth and old age. His was more the physiological approach, and he observed, "The diseases of young men are more acute and curable, of old men longer and hard to cure: a young man's wounds soon close, an old man's later; . . . because old men's bodies do neither perspire well, nor assimilate well."

We can follow concepts of aging through the emergence and development of modern experimental biology. Aging has never been the major interest of the community of biologists, but those most interested in this field have frequently attempted to describe or explain aging processes in terms of those general biological phenomena which were under intensive study, or which seemed most important at a given time. Thus, when development and growth began to receive a great amount of attention, Weismann and others distinguished between the germ plasm, which is immortal, and the soma, which ages. Minot perceived a relationship between growth and aging, in that senescence appeared to be related to the slowing or cessation of growth. Similarly, Child observed that senescence in metazoans was not inevitable—it could apparently be inhibited by both growth and regeneration.

When the importance of microorganisms in disease was appreciated, the notion that aging was caused by toxic products from intestinal bacteria was taken seriously by Metchnikoff and others of his day. The discovery of hormones promoted the "monkey gland" era, during which it was believed that aging was due to endocrine failure, and that gland transplantation or hormone injections would have rejuvenating effects. When biologists were learning chemistry, particularly protein structure and the behavior of colloids, it was argued by Heilbrun and many others that aging was caused by dehydration or syneresis of body colloids. In the present era of molecular biology, aging processes are frequently discussed in terms of altered gene transcription, translation, and somatic mutation.

In recent decades there has been a relative decrease in reflections and a priori conclusions about aging, and extensive efforts have been made to obtain data on aging systems by experiments and observations. The realization has also grown that the aging of human beings, which is of major concern to most of us, represents aspects or manifestations of many basic processes operating at a variety of levels, and in a variety of organisms and living systems.

The accumulation of empirical data has been enormous. Nathan Shock compiled a bibliography on aging for the years 1949–1955 which contained 15,983 references. A number of books have been written which have attempted to bring much of this material together and organize it in some meaningful way. Notable among these are Alex

Comfort's *The Biology of Senescence,* and *Time, Cells, and Aging* by Bernard Strehler. An impressive list of review articles and symposium volumes has also been produced in recent years.

The writing of this book at this time is based on the conviction that we now know enough about aging to argue mechanisms and present some probable cause and effect sequences. We have acquired so much information about some types of aging that it is no longer sufficient merely to catalogue the various findings and list the possible mechanisms, any more than it was sufficient in the last century to argue mechanisms in the absence of knowledge. Although there are some aging systems we know almost nothing about, and there are large gaps of knowledge concerning the systems we know the most about, we do know what kinds of questions to ask. In most cases, in addition, we can advance reasonable hypotheses and utilize conceptual frameworks that we can test by new observations. We are also beginning to realize what types of experiments should be performed to obtain the most useful information. One purpose of this book is an attempt to judge the significance of certain types of studies in relation to major questions about aging.

Previous books on aging have, almost without exception, been written for the committed gerontologist, or have been aimed at the practicing biologist or physician who would like to know something about aging. No textbook on aging exists. Aging processes now constitute a definable and recognizable area or discipline. This book is written for the biologist, early in his career, who wants to learn the essentials of this area.

Considering the massive accumulation of journals each week, it could be argued that no single author knows enough to write an up-to-date and thorough book about anything. Such an argument would be particularly valid in the case of aging, which deals with almost all biological subjects, and in addition, is concerned with rates of change and progression of processes in all living systems. An attempt has been made to minimize the hazards of a one-author effort by focusing on mammalian systems. Every type of aging process can be found in a mammal. References to aging in lower forms are made when they are relevant to certain important concepts, questions, or theses. The emphasis on mammalian systems, however, negates the responsibility for attempting critical evaluations of studies on such forms as plants, bacteria, bryozoans, insects, or amphibians; although concepts arising from consideration of mammalian systems will apply to these organisms as well.

In dealing with mammalian systems no attempt has been made to achieve encyclopedic coverage. Access to the literature is provided in the selected references at ends of chapters, and with illustrations. References have been selected because they appear to bear on important or key questions and concepts about mechanisms of aging, or because they are representative of the types of studies undertaken in certain areas. In many cases equally appropriate investigations by other workers could have been cited.

This book contains both facts and hypotheses—hopefully, distinguished from each other. Very few of the explanations of biological phenomena that we accept as proved could actually survive a rigorously logical criticism. Mechanisms are often considered proved if there is agreement that a cause-and-effect sequence exists, that they are not contradicted by any facts, and that they are capable of explaining major manifestations of the phenomenon in question. These criteria have been used here in advancing and criticizing hypotheses about aging. One item of new information can demolish a hypothesis constructed over decades and based on hundreds of observations. It is hoped that this book will stimulate thinking about aging processes, and the search for new items of information.

ONE

Characteristics of Aging

Processes

A property that all aging systems share is that of progressive and irreversible change. Nonaging systems are those that appear the same to us as we examine them from time to time, even though dynamic processes may comprise the system. If two chemicals A and B interact to give products C and D by a reversible reaction, the reaction will proceed until certain amounts of the four components are present, the amounts depending on starting concentrations and how much free energy is released or absorbed in the reaction. Similarly, starting with C and D, the reaction will yield A and B, and will proceed until certain amounts of the four components are obtained. The reaction at thermodynamic equilibrium is represented in Fig. 1.1. If no work is done on

Fig. 1.1 A chemical reaction at equilibrium. $A + B \rightleftharpoons C + D$

the system, and environmental conditions are kept constant, the same amount of each component in the same physical state will be present next week and next year. We can observe no change in the system with time. Such a system does not age, because the reaction is reversible. It is unlikely that many such equilibria occur outside of chemistry laboratories, which is why it is difficult to find examples of nonaging systems in nature. In nature, environmental conditions change, systems do work, or have work done on them by other systems, and components are removed from or added to reactions.

The type of nonaging system that we usually observe in nature, particularly in living systems, is a steady-state process (Fig. 1.2). This

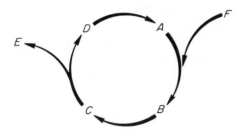

Fig. 1.2   A steady-state process.

process consists of several different reactions, each of which may be reversible. However, the reaction is driven in one direction by the continuous addition of component F and removal of E. A steady state is attained when the amount of F added is balanced by the amount of E removed. The amount of each component will not change with time, although we can tell nothing about the rates of the various reactions by determining amounts of the components present at any instant. If rates do not change, the steady state represents a nonaging system. A progressive and irreversible change in rate of utilization of F and production of E would make this an aging system, even though amounts of components $A, B, C,$ and D remained constant.

It may not appear to make sense to talk about aging or nonaging of a steady-state process, because the process contains different populations at different times. For example, the molecules of compounds in the Krebs cycle proceed through the cycle and are replaced by new molecules. Since the system is continually being renewed, what is there to age or not to age? This is a conceptual problem that is frequently encountered when one is considering the aging of a cell whose components are turning over, or the aging of an organism whose cells are being replaced. The problem serves to point out that aging can be most readily perceived and appreciated when it occurs in a substance or structure that remains present and can be observed as it undergoes change. However, as will be dealt with in later sections, a system or organization has an identity and properties of its own, somewhat independent of the turnover of its components, and progressive changes can occur in function and efficiency of such systems. In some cases, perhaps eventually in all, aging of such a system can be traced to changes in some nonrenewable component in a second system that has some regulatory influence on the first.

A functional or physiological counterpart of the steady state is seen in the maintenance of homeostasis. Here, various processes counteract each other to maintain some factor or activity at a steady optimal level. The factor to be maintained may be body temperature, blood sugar, intracellular calcium, blood cell concentration, or any of the thousands of other structures and metabolites that cannot vary beyond certain limits without being incompatible with life. Processes that raise the level of some factor are opposed by reactions that diminish the level. Figure 1.3 indicates the fluctuations of some property or sub-

Fig. 1.3   The maintenance of homeostasis.

stance around an optimal level with the passage of time. This represents a nonaging system as long as the level around which the deviations occur remain constant, and as long as the deviations occur at the same rates. Many such mechanisms appear not to age when examined over short time intervals. However, long-term observations may reveal a progressive alteration in the mean level or increasing sluggishness in the reestablishment of the level following displacements.

Aging versus developmental and abnormal processes

Aging, then, can be represented by a single arrow, while non-aging processes are at equilibrium or in a steady state. Although all aging processes are progressive and irreversible under usual conditions, it will be apparent that there are systems which undergo progressive change which are not generally thought of as aging. Growth and development of living systems must be considered in this connection. The border line between development and aging is frequently indistinct. One is free to use any definition that is convenient and can be made clear to others. Development could be considered a form of aging, or aging could be thought of as a continuation of development. It is often useful, however, to attempt a distinction between the two. Developmental processes are usually not steadily progressive, but slow down or stop, the state of maturity being defined by the cessation or slowing of such processes. Aging processes tend to begin or accelerate at maturity, although they may be in evidence at earlier stages. By teleological criteria, development can be viewed as consisting of early processes that enhance the functional capacities of a system, whereas aging consists of later processes that diminish, or have no effect on, ability to function. Essentially all processes that are steadily progressive turn out to be harmful to the system involved.

Other steadily progressing processes, which are not usually considered to represent aging, are certain diseases. These are referred to as "diseases" because they occur in only a fraction of a population. If they occurred in all members of a population, they would be called "aging processes." This brings us to another important criterion of an aging process: It is a normal process, in that it occurs in all members of the population under consideration.

We can now define an aging process as one that occurs in all members of a population, that is progressive and irreversible under usual conditions, and that begins or accelerates at maturity in those systems which undergo growth and development.

End points

As a system ages, changes occur in its properties, organization, and composition. These changes can be observed from time to time, and rates of aging can be determined. Frequently, however, progressive alterations result in a very abrupt change or end point in the state of a system. Such end points are often used in the study of aging processes. Examples would be the burning out of a light bulb or the death of a cell or animal.

If aging processes are proceeding in all members of a population, and if they are responsible for attainment of an end point, the amount of time required (or age) for end points in the population should give an approximately normal frequency distribution (Fig. 1.4). If the end point is death, whether of light bulb, storage battery, insect, or human being, the modal value in Fig. 1.4 can be considered the mean life span of the population.

Using the ages at end point from Fig. 1.4, we can plot the percentage of the population at each age which has not reached the end point. If the end point is death, the percentage of those surviving can be plotted as a function of age (Fig. 1.5). A rather rectangular curve is

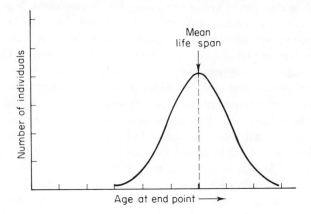

Fig. 1.4 **Number of individuals in an aging population reaching an end point as a function of time.**

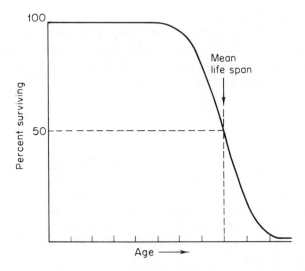

Fig. 1.5 Percent survival as a function of time for an aging population.

obtained, which indicates mean life span by the 50 percent survival point.

By dividing the total life span into a number of short intervals, the data of Fig. 1.5 can be used to calculate how many are surviving at the beginning of each interval, and what percentage of these attain the end point, or die, during the interval. These values plotted against age give the age-specific death rate. Figure 1.6 shows both the rate and probability of dying of members of an aging population, as a function

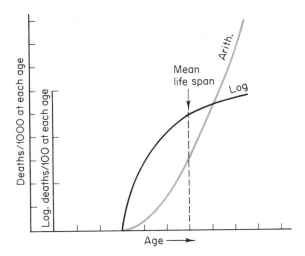

Fig. 1.6 Rate and probability of attaining end points for an aging population as a function of time.

of age. The log of the age-specific death rate is included in Fig. 1.6. The log curve becomes approximately linear after the mean life span, indicating that the rate and probability of dying doubles at regular intervals during this period.

These curves would be obtained only in the case of a rather homogeneous population, one in which the same aging processes were occurring in all the members at approximately equal rates, and in which the end points were the result of the same processes in all the individuals. Few populations in nature are so homogeneous. In particular, end points, or deaths, may be due to different processes in different individuals. This results in a skewing of the frequency distribution, and variations in the shapes of percent survival and age-specific death rate curves. If such curves are plotted for a population under study, a great deal can be inferred about consequences of aging processes, rates of aging, the effect of environmental changes, and the role of programming or genetics in the dying out of populations.

End points may have no relationship to aging processes. An example might be drinking glasses. A large number of these could exist at a given time, and, with the passage of time, the probability of being broken could have nothing to do with how old the individuals were. Similarly, a population of organisms may die out by an infection, and the susceptibility to infection or its severity may have nothing to do with the age of affected organisms. In such cases the same percentage of those present at the beginning of every time interval would be expected to attain the end point during that interval. This would hold for all intervals. There would be no increase with increasing age, as seen in populations where end points are due to aging processes. The age-specific death rate would then be a horizontal line. The percent survival curve would take the form of Fig. 1.7. This is the same

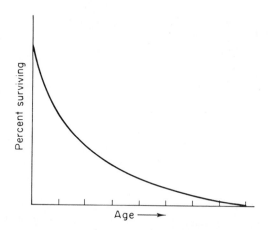

Fig. 1.7 Percent surviving as a function of time for a population in which the probability of reaching end points remains constant with time. End points are not caused by aging processes.

curve as that for the velocity of a first-order chemical reaction as a function of time. It tells us that the number of individuals dying at each interval is proportional to those present, and that the proportionality is constant with the passage of time.

As mentioned above, few populations in nature will give a percent survival curve as rectangular as Fig. 1.5. In even fewer populations, perhaps none, is the end point completely accidental—that is, having no relationship to age. It turns out that most populations yield percent survival curves that fall somewhere between the curve of Fig. 1.5 for age-caused end points and the curve of Fig. 1.7 for accidental, non-age-related end points. By inspecting such curves for real populations, much can be learned about the relative importance of accidental and age-related processes in causing death or other end points.

TWO

Chemical Aging

Understanding the mechanisms of biological aging must ultimately depend on knowing the changes that occur with time to molecules that comprise living systems. Furthermore, it is most likely that these chemical changes are of types that have been studied and about which quite a bit is known. That is, there would appear to be little justification at this point for looking for a new type of chemistry to explain aging at higher levels of organization. The ways in which substances can change with time are quite limited. The problems are in knowing exactly which biologically important ions and molecules undergo these changes, in knowing the specific reactions involved, and in relating the chemical changes to alterations in function of the living systems.

It would be difficult to avoid the conclusion that the primary, or most fundamental, changes most likely occur in nondynamic or non-renewable substances. Or, more simply, for something to age, it must remain present—or at least the rate of aging must be greater than the rate of replacement. The only exception might be the accumulation of alterations in a self-replicating molecule or structure.

Molecular turnover, as will be dealt with in later sections, is widespread in living systems. We would not expect a population of continuously replaced non-self-replicating molecules to be the fundamental site of aging. On the other hand, such a population could demonstrate age-changes as a consequence of primary changes in other molecules. Such secondary changes would usually be in terms of concentrations. For example, an enzyme that participates in the synthesis of some molecule might become inactive with time. This would result in a decreased concentration of the molecule, even though it is turning over. Similarly, if a system responsible for degradation became inactive, the substance being degraded would increase in concentration.

It is also apparent that there is a relationship between complexity and progressive change, both in chemical systems and in living organisms. There are more ways in which complex substances and systems can change; the ease with which aging processes can be discerned is frequently related to the level of organization of a substance or system. Thus, we do not observe age-changes in subatomic particles, atoms, or ions. Radioactive decay represents change in a population of atoms and could be considered an aging process. However, the end point of atomic disintegration is not a result of an aging process. The event of disintegration is random; the probability of its occurrence has no relationship to how long the atom has been in existence. If the number of atoms that have not disintegrated (i.e., the percentage surviving) is plotted against time, a first-order reaction curve of the type shown in Fig. 1.7 is obtained. This indicates end points that are not age-dependent.

In the preceding chapter a distinction was made between a reaction at equilibrium and an aging process. This distinction holds only for those reactions that have attained equilibrium, and in which constant amounts of reactants and products can be identified. In the strictest sense there are probably no completely irreversible chemical reactions. Reactions usually considered to be irreversible are those in which we can observe the disappearance of reactants and the accumulation of products, to the point where the reactants are present in very small amounts or cannot be measured. The arrow indicating reversal of the reaction is very short. Aging processes at the molecular level are generally of this type.

Crystals

Perhaps the simplest example of aging involves the progressive formation of ionic crystals. Ions in solution become arranged so that each ion is surrounded by the largest possible number of oppositely charged ions, and all charges are neutralized in the resulting lattice. Such a lattice will demonstrate a periodicity in arrangement of ions, and the composition of the repeat units will depend on the size of the ions involved. In sodium chloride crystals each ion is surrounded by six ions of opposite charge. A crystal may be composed of a large number of different types of ions, as well as water molecules (water of hydration), and may have other types of ions adsorbed to the surface, where reversible reactions frequently occur. Hydroxyapatite is a widespread inorganic crystal in animals. Its lattice is composed of four different ions, and additional ions are adsorbed to the surface, where exchange with ions in solution takes place. Organic molecules also form crystals in which molecules are held together by covalent bonds or van der Waal's forces.

Movement of ions and molecules is restricted in crystals. Ions from solution will enter a crystal and the latter will grow, as long as the concentration of ions in solution is above a certain level. While exchange may take place at the surface of the crystal, ions and molecules deeper in the lattice are inaccessible and will persist. Whether or not crystal formation is an aging process depends on persistence of components and progression, or growth, of the lattice. If ions in solution are maintained at steady-state concentrations and environmental conditions are stable, the system will age by crystal growth. Reversal of such a process would require the addition of new regulatory mechanisms.

Macromolecular aggregations

Similar crystallization processes occur with molecules of greater complexity. Large and complex molecules—protein, nucleic acid, lipid and carbohydrate—comprise the bulk of biological chemicals. Many of these exist as high polymers, that is, in linear arrays of repeating units. Such polymers frequently contain segments with the configuration, reactive groups, and charges that enable them to form crystals with corresponding segments of other polymer chains. As shown in Fig. 2.1, individual polymers will exist early in solution or in an

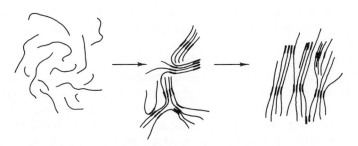

Fig. 2.1 Amorphous polymer forming oriented crystalline polymer.

amorphous state. With the passage of time, crystalline regions will appear where the polymer molecules are held together. Finally, the entire structure may become oriented, with periodic crystalline zones. As in the case of inorganic crystals, polymers become increasingly insoluble with crystallization. Bonds holding the subunits together in the crystalline zones may be covalent, hydrogen, ionic, van der Waal's forces, or a combination of these. Formation of such crystals is facilitated by exertion of tensile stress on the system. Once an ordered structure is attained, there is an opportunity for more bonds or cross links to form between the linear polymers. Consequently, aging is manifested by an increasing crystallinity, decreasing solubility, and alterations in other properties which depend on the number and location of cross links, which tend to maintain the structure in a given configuration. Again, as with inorganic crystals, such an aggregation of subunits will occur naturally in accord with thermodynamic principles, unless additional factors are imposed on the system.

Aggregation of molecules with the formation of cross links is a particularly widespread aging process. It is responsible for the aging of rubber, plastics, leather, paper, and paint. Attempts are often made to inhibit aging of such nonliving systems by slowing or controlling interactions by various treatments. Since animals contain high concentrations of molecules that can undergo these aggregations, they are faced with the same problems.

The formation and growth of polymer chains themselves represent an example of chemical aging. Molecules with functional groups, particularly unsaturated hydrocarbons, will frequently react with each other to yield chains of increasing length and decreasing solubility. The resulting polymer may consist of different molecules, as is seen in polyester and polyamide, polymerized by ester and amide bonds, respectively. Or the polymer may be composed of a single type of molecule, as is often the case when polymerization of molecules containing the vinyl group ($CH_2 = CH-$) occurs. Polymerization of unsaturated hydrocarbons may be accelerated by oxidation or light. Control of aging processes of these types is the basis of the synthetic rubber, resin, and plastic industries.

Closely related to the processes of polymer formation and crystallization is the formation of insoluble complex compounds. Such compounds may not have the ordered structure of polymers and crystals, although their formation would occur by the same types of reactions and would have the same consequences in regard to solubility and other properties. Insolubility of products would tend to characterize these reactions as aging processes, since reversal would be minimized. The products formed could be quite heterogeneous. Proteins, inorganic ions, and nucleic acids could aggregate. Or carbohydrates and lipids would be expected to react with each other. Because of the variety of functional groups and potential bonds available in biological molecules and ions, it would be possible for very large aggregates to form. These could contain ionic crystals, polymers, and complex macromolecules.

Denaturation

Complex macromolecules may be characterized by their chemical composition, or primary structure. In addition, however, such molecules may contain chains with zones of highly ordered coiling (secondary structure), and the chains themselves may be folded or twisted into specific configurations (tertiary structure). Such complex configurations have been studied most thoroughly in proteins, where they are essential for biological activity. Specific configurations are maintained by a variety of chemical bonds. These molecules are susceptible to alterations of configuration with time, such that they lose biological activity and demonstrate different physical properties. The altered, or "denatured," molecules are generally less soluble, more symmetrical, more easily degraded, and they demonstrate reactive groups that were previously masked or inaccessible.

Denaturation is believed to be due to rupture of bonds that hold components of the molecule in specific folded configurations, with a consequent unfolding to a more random state. Change from the native to the denatured state is associated with a marked increase in entropy. Denaturation will thus tend to occur naturally with the passage of time. Some proteins can remain undenatured and at thermodynamic equilibrium for indefinite periods if environmental conditions are held constant within narrow limits. Such environmental control probably does not exist outside of laboratories. Denaturation can be greatly accelerated by such agents as heat, light, increased pressure, surface tension, dehydration, and chemicals that rupture hydrogen bonds.

Mechanical wear and tear

Structures of macromolecules subjected to repeated and prolonged stresses may be damaged. Membranes and fibers may become fragmented or split, or may develop perforations.

Mutations

The concept of mutation is a familiar one because of the growth of modern genetics. It denotes an alteration in a macromolecule which persists, and which causes a change in biological function. Mutations have been studied most extensively in nucleic acids, but there is no good reason why similar changes could not occur in other macromolecules. A mutation may take place at the time of synthesis of a molecule. A bond may rupture in a large molecule, or may form at an abnormal site. Chemical groups may be cleaved off, or oxidized, or reduced. A large number of mutations is theoretically possible in the case of any large molecule, and would be expected to occur in the nature of accidents. In addition, the rate of mutation can be greatly accelerated by ionizing radiation and by certain chemical agents. A population of macromolecules would thus contain an increasing percentage of altered molecules with the passage of time.

Concentration changes

When a system contains two or more components or populations of molecules, it may age, not by changes in individual molecules, but by changes in relative concentrations. Aging of this type may occur in nonrenewable populations or in systems in which molecular turnover occurs. As mentioned earlier, primary age-changes occurring in an enzyme important in synthesis or degradation of a molecule would result in changing concentrations of that molecule. Even in the absence of any primary changes, differential rates of synthesis and/or degradation of different components would cause a progressive change in proportions of components within the system. The system would thus be considered an aging one. In a system of any complexity, it is clear that for aging of this type not to occur, rates of synthesis and degradation must be balanced for each component. Even a very slight inbalance in turnover of one component will, with the passage of time, cause an increasingly conspicuous aging of the system.

An extreme example of aging of this type, and one related to crystallization, or aggregation of subunits, is merely the accumulation of a substance. This occurs when one of the components in a mixed population can be formed but cannot be degraded at the rate of other components.

Some additional generalities

It is apparent that some of the characterizations of an aging system discussed in Ch. 1 lose precision when applied at the molecular level. It should be emphasized that these criteria and definitions hold best for complex systems and, like most attempts at categorization, are not entirely satisfactory in all cases. Crystal formation, the accumulation of substances, changes in concentrations, and macromolecular aggregations, when progressive and irreversible, constitute aging processes by earlier definitions. Some forms of denaturation, in which the rupture of many bonds is required, may represent aging end points, in that the probability of occurrence increases with time. On the other hand, mutations and other denaturations may be instantaneous rather than progressive. Further, the reaction may be a random hit process, with a probability of occurrence unrelated to the age of the molecule. In such cases, it is useful to consider the system, or population of molecules, as aging. Aging end points, if they occur, would then be apparent at higher levels of organization than that of individual molecules.

The relevance to aging of the types of chemical reactions described here is that living systems contain many molecules that can undergo these changes. Essentially all biological chemicals can participate in such molecular aging. Furthermore, these reactions tend to occur naturally or spontaneously with the passage of time. Thus, the question is not how a living system can age chemically, but rather which aging processes are permitted to occur and which are inhibited or have their consequences reversed by additional processes. If aging processes did not occur, there would be no reason why a complex living system could not persist in a steady state indefinitely.

THREE

Extracellular Aging

The extracellular compartment

Large amounts of body components are outside of cells. The size of this extracellular compartment is difficult to measure. However, an approximation can be arrived at on the basis of water determinations. In a mammal, body water is about 70 percent of the body weight. Of this, about 50 percent of the body weight is intracellular water. The remaining 20 percent, the extracellular water, is in two compartments— 5 percent in the blood plasma, and 15 percent that is extracellular and extravascular. Our interest in aging will concern us with this tissue extracellular compartment. Assuming values obtained from tendon measurements of 65 percent water and 35 percent solids in this compartment, and considering the extracellular water to be 15 percent of the body weight, we arrive at a figure of about 23 percent of the body for the weight or volume for this extracellular tissue compartment.

The fractions of tissues and organs which are extracellular vary enormously from one site to another. Perhaps 80 percent or more of skin, bone, tendon, ligaments, and fascia is extracellular. At the other extreme, organs such as liver, kidney, and muscle have extracellular values at or considerably below the mean value of 23 percent. The physical state of this compartment also varies a great deal, depending on the components present and their organization. Extracellular material may be semisolid or colloidal, elastic, tough, fibrous, or hard.

Extracellular components fall into two classes: those which are passing through, and those which are structural constituents and which characterize this compartment. Among the substances passing through

20

are all of the inorganic ions from the blood, particularly sodium, chloride, and bicarbonate in high concentrations. Plasma proteins, notably albumin, also filter into the extracellular compartment. Substances that pass between cells and blood or lymphatic vessels must travel through an extracellular compartment. This would include all metabolites, nutrients, hormones, and gases.

The structural or characteristic components of the extracellular compartment comprise the connective tissue. At the junction between epithelial or endothelial cells and the connective tissue, there is usually a basement membrane. Little is known about this membrane, except that it is rich in glycoprotein, and is probably important in regulating the passage of materials to and from cells. The connective tissue itself contains inorganic ions and additional poorly characterized proteins and glycoproteins in low concentrations. The major components of connective tissue have been well studied. These are the fibrous proteins, collagen, reticulin, and elastin—and the mucopolysaccharides. These substances are all probably synthesized by mesodermal cells, the fibroblasts, and are all high polymers.

Acid mucopolysaccharides

The polysaccharides present in the highest concentrations— and those studied most thoroughly—are polymers of disaccharides. There are at least six of these. They are listed with the composition of repeating units and distribution in Fig. 3.1. The highly polymerized particles vary considerably in molecular configuration and molecular weight, as well as in concentrations in different tissues. Particle weights as high as 8×10^6 have been described for hyaluronic acid. Molecular weights and configuration determine physical properties of the polymers. The polysaccharides exist as greatly hydrated gels, such that the space they fill is enormous compared to what would be expected for the unhydrated molecules. Hyaluronic acid is highly viscous and is found in high concentrations in mobile tissues and wherever lubrication is required. On the other hand, the hydrated chondroitin sulfates are turgid, and provide tissues with a combination of firmness and some flexibility.

The mucopolysaccharides appear to be synthesized and degraded quite rapidly. Half lives of from a couple of days to a month have been described for various polysaccharides at different sites. Turnover studies have been carried out almost entirely with tissues such as cartilage, dermis, tendon, and bone. Essentially nothing is known about turnover rates of mucopolysaccharides in parenchymatous organs.

Substance		Site
Hyaluronic acid	(→ 4 glucuronic acid β1-3 acetyl glucosamine β1 →)	Ubiquitous in connective tissue (?), skin, tendon, synovial fluid, vitreous humor, ligamentus nuchae, heart valve, aorta
Chondroitin sulfate A	(→ 4 glucuronic acid β1-3 acetyl galactosamine-4 sulfate β1 →)	Cartilage, bone, cornea, aorta, ligamentum nuchae
Chondroitin sulfate B	(→ 4 L-iduronic acid β1-3 acetyl galactosamine-4 sulfate β1 →)	Skin, heart valves, cartilage, tendon, cornea, aorta, lung, ligamentum nuchae
Chondroitin sulfate C	(→ 4 glucuronic acid β1-3 acetyl galactosamine-6 sulfate β1 →)	Cartilage, sclera, bone, tendon, heart valve
Keratosulfate	(→ 3 galactose β1-4 acetyl glucosamine-6 sulfate β1 →)	Cornea, rib cartilage, bone, nucleus pulposus
Heparitin sulfate	[glucuronic acid, iduronic acid 1 → 4, glucosamine, *N*-acetyl, *N*-sulfate, α-linkages(?), variable composition]	Aorta, lung, liver

Fig. 3.1 Repeating polymeric units and sites of major deposition of acid mucopolysaccharides of connective tissue. (From paper by Sobel.)

Fibrous proteins of connective tissue

The major proteins of mammalian connective tissue are collagen, reticulin, and elastin. Reticulin may be considered a variety of collagen, as its most significant difference from typical collagen is that it is bound to appreciable amounts of lipid and carbohydrate. A discussion of collagen will probably apply to reticulin as well. We shall consider collagen in some detail because it may be very important in its own right in mammalian aging, and because it can serve as a model for the types of age-changes that can occur in polymerized, relatively inert macromolecules.

A great deal is known about the chemistry of collagen. This is because collagen is the source of leather, gelatin, and, in previous years, of glue. Scientists in these industries were carrying out extensive studies of collagen while biologists considered the extracellular proteins as merely inert packing that must be gotten rid of to facilitate the study of isolated cellular systems. In recent decades biologists have come to realize that collagen comprises 25 to 30 percent of the total body protein, and is of importance in organ function as well as in many pathological processes.

Collagen is an unusual protein in that about one-third of its amino acid residues consists of proline plus hydroxyproline, and another third is glycine. It is poor in sulfur-containing amino acids. Tropocollagen, the basic collagen molecule, is rod-shaped, approximately 3000 Å long, and 15 Å in diameter. It has a molecular weight of about 300,000. The molecule is composed of three polypeptide chains, each with a molecular weight of approximately 100,000, which are arranged in a left-handed helix. Shortly after synthesis, the molecules undergo a side-to-side aggregation. They may also polymerize end to end, although this point is not settled at present. Most of this aggregation and polymerization occurs in the extracellular compartment after tropocollagen molecules are extruded from fibroblasts. The lateral aggregation occurs with adjacent molecules one-quarter of their length out of phase with each other in a staggered arrangement. This results in a periodicity of about 640 Å in dried fibrils which can be seen by electron microscopy (Fig. 3.2). The building up of subunits proceeds to the formation of fibrils. Fibril bundles are then formed to the point where

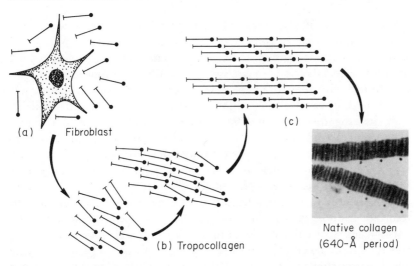

(a) Fibroblast

(c)

(b) Tropocollagen

Native collagen
(640-Å period)

Fig. 3.2 The formation of collagen fibers. [From Gross, J., cited in article by Seifter and Gallop, Figure 10, page 242, in The Proteins, Volume IV, (Second Edition).]

gross fibers may be identified in many organs and tissues. At the ultra-structural level, zones of crystallinity alternate with amorphous regions. This arrangement is frequently observed in oriented polymers, as noted in Ch. 1.

When collagen is first synthesized there is very little cross linking between peptide chains within tropocollagen molecules, and no cova-lent bonds between molecules that have aggregated. As the collagen matures, additional intra- and intermolecular cross links form. There is evidence that links in both locations form by a single continuous process. If young or growing tissue is extracted with a neutral salt solution, appreciable amounts of collagen go into solution. This repre-sents tropocollagen, or poorly cross-linked aggregates. As the tissue becomes more mature, less and less of the collagen is extractable. Finally, in the mature tissue, collagen subunits are firmly bound into fibrils, and only traces may be extracted.

The types of cross links that form in collagen have received a great deal of attention because of their role in determining the properties of fibrils. It has been shown that hydrogen bonds and short-range forces dependent on steric factors are of importance. In addition, many dif-ferent types of covalent bonds, some involving hexose derivatives, have been implicated in the cross linking of collagen subunits. Recent data suggest that two types of covalent bond may be of particular sig-nificance. One involves a nonhelical peptide at the end of the tropo-collagen molecule. A second is believed to result from an aldol condensation between two lysyl-derived aldehydes on adjacent peptide chains. The aldehydes may be formed by the oxidative deamination of lysine.

When it was first appreciated that most body proteins were in a dynamic state—that is, continually turning over—collagen was listed as one of the inert, or nonrenewable, proteins. Experiments in which proteins were labeled with an isotope at birth (isotope content was determined with the passage of time) suggested that once collagen was synthesized, it was not broken down and replaced. In accord with this view, investigators could not find an enzyme in tissues of higher ani-mals that was capable of degrading undenatured collagen. More re-cent studies have shown, however, that collagen may turn over quite rapidly at some sites, such as in the postpartum uterus. Turnover at slower rates has also been detected in other organs. By the use of very sensitive methods, collagen-degrading enzymes have been identified in resorbing tadpole tails, leukocytes, uterus, and bone cells. Accumulated data suggest that collagen exists in at least two metabolic pools. That which is most recently synthesized has an appreciable turnover rate which varies from site to site as a function of physiological alterations and tissue stresses. Most of the body collagen is mature and insoluble, and is either nonrenewable or has an exceedingly low rate of turnover. It would appear that a significant fraction of insoluble collagen remains present for the life of the animal, and should be an excellent candidate for age-related changes.

Understanding the chemistry of elastin has been hindered by its extreme insolubility. It cannot be extracted from tissues by mild extraction procedures, as in the case of tropocollagen. Preliminary isolation is usually by extraction of tissue with hot alkali. The insoluble residue is then used for further purification. Elastin is also an unusual protein in that about 95 percent of its amino acids are nonpolar, and 80 percent of the residues are glycine, alanine, valine, and proline. Elastin fibers appear amorphous by electron microscopy, and are believed to exist as three-dimensional networks of coiled or kinked polypeptide chains held together by covalent bonds. Elastin is probably synthesized in the form of soluble subunits, or so-called proelastin. Proelastin is a hypothetical substance which has not been isolated, and which probably becomes polymerized immediately. Cross links responsible for maturation of elastin include two amino acids: desmosine and isodesmosine. These are formed by the condensation of four lysine residues, three of which have been oxidatively deaminated. Another amino acid implicated in cross links is lysinonorleucine. Recent studies have indicated that aldehyde groups of the type found in collagen also play a role in the cross linking of elastin.

Little data are available on elastin turnover, but it is probably at least as inert as collagen. As would be expected, elastin has the highest concentrations in those tissues that show elastic behavior (Fig. 3.3).

Gels and fibers in tissues

Synthesis of the polysaccharides and protein fibers of connective tissue does not occur at rates that insure constant amounts of the various components in a given tissue. Rates of disappearance are also different for the different components. It has frequently been observed that early in connective tissue development, polysaccharides are found in high concentration. Later, fibrous proteins appear in greater amounts as the concentration of polysaccharides falls. This has led to the view that mucopolysaccharides may play a role in orientation and organization of the fibrous proteins.

As noted above, there is great variation in content and composition of connective tissue at different sites. Connective tissue constitutes the bulk of bone, cartilage, skin, tendon, and ligaments. It is present in very high concentrations in lung and blood vessels. If sections of parenchymatous organs are stained for mucopolysaccharides and fi-

Tissue	Species	Elastin (%) [a]
Aorta	Ox	40
Aorta	Pig	57
Aorta	Rat	48
Aorta (thoracic)	Dog	29–32
Aorta (abdominal)	Dog	11–16
Pulmonary arteries	Dog	16–20
Spleen	Ox	5
Spleen	Pig	1.2
Spleen	Rat	0.6
Lung (10–30 years)	Human	4
Lung (45–58 years)	Human	7
Lung (64–70 years)	Human	10
Lung (78–94 years)	Human	14
Lung	Human	19
Yellow ligaments (lumbar tract) (25–37 years)	Human	70
Yellow ligaments (lumbar tract) (45–68 years)	Human	56

[a] On dry weight basis.

Fig. 3.3   Elastin content of various tissues. (Modified from paper by Seifter and Gallop.)

brous proteins, it is found that thin zones of connective tissue occur around cells and blood vessels of all sizes. An exception is the brain, where the neurones and glial cells are not surrounded by connective tissue, but where the usual pattern of connective tissue in the walls of vessels and in perivascular location is observed.

The amounts of collagen and elastin present depend on the function of the tissue. Collagen maintains form, provides strength, and limits deformations, and is present in high concentrations where these factors are required. Elastin is a prominent component of mobile and distensible tissues. The extracellular space of lung and its relationships are shown in Fig. 3.4. Polysaccharide is not demonstrated by this technique, but the elastin and collagen content, and the dimensions of this space between two basement membranes can be appreciated. It is clear that muscle contraction and tissue pulsations of all types must occur within a matrix of connective tissue, and that all materials passing between cell and vessel must go through connective tissue. Function of connective tissue will be dealt with again in later sections dealing with mechanisms of mammalian aging.

Several generations ago, students of aging noted that connective tissue in the aged appeared dried out, or more fibrillar and advanced

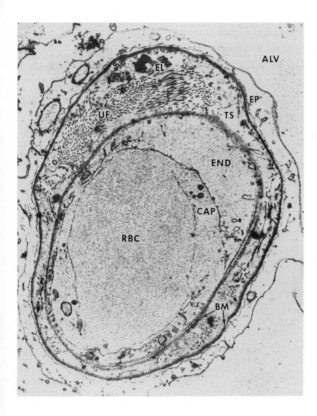

Fig. 3.4 Human lung by electron microscopy. ALV — alveolus, EP — epithelium, TS — tissue extracellular space, BM — basement membranes, EL — elastin, UF — unit fiber (collagen), END — endothelium, CAP — capillary lumen, RBC — red blood cell. (From Low. 1961. Anat. Rec. 139: 105.)

the notion that aging was due to dehydration or syneresis of body colloids. We are now in a position to attempt explanations of these observations in more precise terms.

Quantitative age-changes

Composition of the extracellular space is probably never in a steady state. Different substances are synthesized and degraded at varying rates, and the amounts of serum and cellular components diffusing through are undoubtedly not constant. We are concerned with progressive and irreversible changes that satisfy the criteria of aging processes. It may be difficult to identify such changes in the extracellular compartment because of certain pathological processes that are age-influenced and are widespread in mammals. The late stage of all inflammatory reactions is characterized by the synthesis of connective tissue polysaccharides and proteins. When such reactions occur in all members of a population, and are progressive, we may consider them as true aging processes.

If total extracellular water is measured by thiocyanate diffusion space, it is found that there is a general decrease with age in human beings (Fig. 3.5). The scatter of points is quite typical in such measure-

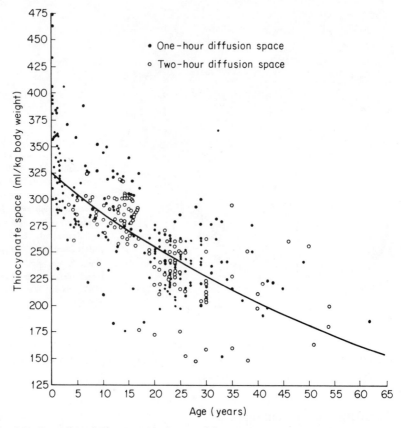

Fig. 3.5   Extracellular body water (thiocyanate diffusion space) as a function of age in human beings. (From Biological Handbook, Blood and Other Body Fluids. 1961. Federation of American Societies for Experimental Biology.)

ments of human populations. Since the plasma volume does not change significantly with age, there appears to be a conspicuous decline in tissue extracellular water. The question that arises is whether this represents a shrinkage of the extracellular compartment, or whether the compartment becomes dehydrated. Measurements of inorganic ion concentrations in a variety of human organs as a function of age have shown increased concentrations of sodium, calcium, and chloride in older organs. Since these are predominantly extracellular ions, it seems reasonable to conclude that the extracellular compartment increases in size with age. Decreases have been found in the concentration of the intracellular ions potassium, magnesium, and phosphate. These data suggest that with age there is a loss or shrinkage of cells within organs, with a concurrent increase in the extracellular compartment. More recent studies of wasting or atrophying muscle, as occurs in several diseases as well as with age, have shown relative increases in extracellular substances. It should be noted that such increases do not necessarily denote increased syntheses, or increased absolute amounts, but appear to be consequences of the loss of cellular volume. Such data do not help explain the apparent loss of extracellular water demonstrated by whole-body measurements, and are actually in conflict with these measurements.

Human tendon is almost all extracellular. Its changes with age can be recognized by gross examination. In the young it appears turgid, and seems to consist of homogeneous bundles or meshworks. In the aged, it appears much more fibrous and dried out. However, when water content is measured, no significant differences between young and old are found. This suggests that the changes in appearance must be related to how organic substances are hydrated, and to the distribution of water within the tissues, rather than to simple water content. Only a limited number of measurements have been made on water content of fibrous connective tissue, and it is possible that some sites will show a conspicuous loss of water with age. However, with currently available data, we cannot explain apparent whole-body water loss on the basis of loss from such tissue.

Bone contains a large fraction of the extracellular compartment in mammals. Developing bone is about 60 percent water, whereas very old cortical bone contains about 10 percent water. The mechanism for loss of water has not been studied extensively. It may be that water is simply replaced by collagen and polysaccharides, and by inorganic crystal growth during maturation. It is not known if water loss occurs at greatest rates during maturation or during aging.

We must conclude at this point that although significant amounts of extracellular water appear to be lost with age, we do not know where the losses occur. Bone is a possibility. A possibility also exists that the apparent loss of water is, in part, an artifact. Thiocyanate and other agents used to measure extracellular space may diffuse less efficiently with increasing age, and may give misleadingly low values. There are reasons, to be brought out in later sections, for suspecting that this might be the case. We may also conclude that the extracellular compartment does not age by a generalized shrinkage, but that at most sites it increases in size or remains constant.

Much of what we know about age-related changes in the extracellular compartment comes from studies of human blood vessels.

These studies were undertaken to gain information about arteriosclerosis, but have yielded important data about normal aging as well. Several substances that pass through the extracellular compartment become bound or trapped, and increase in concentration with increasing age. Calcium salts increase conspicuously. If sections of aorta are stained for calcium, a very striking increase in calcification of the media is observed (Fig. 3.6). A large proportion of this salt is probably

Fig. 3.6 Human thoracic aortic stained for calcium (alizarin-red). Reduced slightly from ×35. Upper left, 30-year-old; upper right, 40-year-old; lower left, 59-year-old. (From Bertelsen. 1961. Acta Pathol. et Microbiol. Scand. 51:206.)

bound to elastin, as partially purified aortic elastin contains increased calcium as a function of age (Fig. 3.7). The pulmonary artery shows the same type of age-related increase in calcium, but absolute values are much lower. Similarly, cholesterol and other lipids increase in the intima of aortas, in the absence of frank arteriosclerosis. Much of the lipid is extracellular, although some can be recognized in cells.

The accumulation of calcium salts may be a generalized phenomenon. Crystals of hydroxyapatite form on connective tissue fibrils in the development of bone, and present evidence suggests that calcium

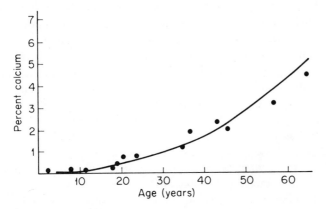

Fig. 3.7 Calcium content of human aortic-elastin as a function of age. (Redrawn from Lansing. 1959. Connective Tissue, Thrombosis, and Atherosclerosis. Academic Press, New York.)

in aging, as well as in diseased tissues, may be in the form of apatite. Mineralization of the extracellular matrix of cartilage is a part of mammalian aging. This may occur to the extent that cartilage is converted to bone. It is not known if mineral deposition occurs with age in the extracellular compartment of parenchymatous organs.

With regard to polysaccharides of the extracellular compartment, it can be stated that many quantitative changes occur with age. However, it is difficult to generalize about these changes. The six acid mucopolysaccharides and neutral glycoproteins have been studied in different tissues of different animals, where different patterns of age-related changes have been discovered. In addition, polysaccharide synthesis is a part of inflammation. Thus, at any site such as the aorta, where chronic inflammation is a part of aging or where intermittent or chronic tissue irritation occurs, increased polysaccharides are found. On the other hand, organs may undergo atrophy or wasting secondary to some other age-related process, with a consequent loss in polysaccharide content. A sample of recent analytical studies in this area reveals the following: The human aorta shows no change in total mucopolysaccharide with age, but hyaluronic acid and chondroitin sulfate decrease, while chondroitin sulfate B and heparitin sulfate increase. In the rat aorta, on the other hand, the hexosamine content increases. Hexosamine decreases in human and rat skin, but remains constant in rat buccal mucosa. Rat tendon shows a decrease in hexosamine, while that of the human shows an increase after 50 years of age. In the case of rat cartilage, sulfur-containing polysaccharides decrease with age while other polysaccharides remain constant.

Sobel has extensively reviewed data of the above type and concludes that, although different tissues demonstrate individual aging characteristics, there is a recognizable pattern in age changes in polysaccharide content, which is a normal component of aging and independent of pathologic processes. It is generally accepted that polysaccharide content is high in newly synthesized connective tissue, and that the concentration falls with maturity. Sobel suggests that after maturity there is a continuing loss of hyaluronic acid. This molecule is hydrated to the extent of 200 to 500 ml of water per gram, and its loss should result in a decrease in the water-holding capacity of the tissue. Since actual water content of tissues has not been shown to change, there may be a redistribution of water such that less is bound to macromolecules. Sobel further suggests that there is an absolute or relative increase in chondroitin sulfate B and heparitin sulfate. He postulates that with maturity, polysaccharide synthesis subsides, but that hyaluronic acid degradation continues to occur because it is not bound to other components. Degradation and loss of sulfated polysaccharides might be inhibited because they are bound to protein.

A useful working hypothesis might be that in the absence of pathological processes, quantitative changes in polysaccharides represent a continuation of developmental processes. These are a decrease in amount of polysaccharide, possibly reflecting hyaluronic acid content, a redistribution of water such that it is not bound and uniform through the connective tissue, but aggregated outside of structural units with a consequent reduction in hydrated gel to fibrous protein ratio. The gel/fiber ratio change has been emphasized by Sobel, and may explain in part the age-related difference in appearance of connective tissue, and may have important functional consequences, which will be discussed in later chapters.

The amount of collagen present is also due to processes that occur at the borderline between normal aging and pathological change. Collagen fibers are synthesized in response to severe or prolonged tissue stresses and are oriented in tissues parallel to lines of stress. Collagen is also formed as part of the healing phase of inflammation. Thus, wherever indolent inflammatory processes occur, a scarring, resulting from collagen synthesis, will be observed. This fibrosis occurs at some sites, particularly in arteries and arterioles, in all members of mammalian populations and should, therefore, be considered an aging process as well as a disease. Analyses of collagen content at these sites have led to the concept that tissue fibrosis is a generalized aspect of aging. However, a variety of collagen determinations in tendon and organs have shown that, in the absence of tissue injury, collagen concentration remains constant with age. It appears that collagen production is regulated by feedback mechanisms which insure that when sufficient collagen is synthesized to maintain form and provide strength in an organ, further production is inhibited, and the amount present remains constant. When more strength is required in damaged or stressed tissue, collagen synthesis is initiated.

Very little is known about elastin concentration or content as a function of age. Several studies are in agreement that elastin concentration increases in human lung, and an apparent decrease has been described in ligament (Fig. 3.3). It is not clear whether such changes are due to gain or loss of other tissue components. Analyses of elastin in old tissue are complicated by the fact that very old collagen appears to have the same solubility characteristics as elastin, and is difficult to separate from the latter.

Aging of collagen

As mentioned earlier, collagen is synthesized as soluble tropocollagen molecules that aggregate to form insoluble collagen fibrils. While an animal is growing, its tissues contain large amounts of neutral salt soluble collagen. With maturation or growth cessation, the soluble collagen drops to very low levels as it is incorporated into mature collagen. This disappearance of soluble collagen has been frequently demonstrated in animals that have attained their species-specific size as well as in animals whose growth has been inhibited.

With the cessation of growth, then, almost all collagen is in the form of mature insoluble fibrils. In the absence of severe tissue stresses or inflammation, the amount of collagen remains constant and demonstrates very little turnover. Since cross linking of collagen subunits occurs in the course of collagen maturation, it might be suspected that some cross linking could continue to occur after the formation of insoluble collagen.

The extent of collagen cross linking can be measured in several ways. By determining the amount of soluble collagen, the earliest stages of cross linking can be determined. However, for measurements of cross linking in insoluble collagen, more indirect methods are required. It has long been known that if collagen fibers are heated to around 62°C, they rapidly contract to a fraction of their original length and take on elasticlike behavior. The contraction is not completely understood, but is thought to depend on melting of crystalline zones in the collagen and on the rupture of hydrogen bonds. A similar contraction when fibers are immersed in a KI solution supports the view that rupture of hydrogen bonds is important. Force of contraction appears to be dependent on the amount of stable cross links. Verzár in 1955 applied this technique to the study of rat tail tendon properties as a function of age. Solids of such tendon consist of over 90 percent collagen, arranged in parallel fibers. He found that the force required to inhibit thermal contraction showed a clear-cut increase with increasing age (Fig. 3.8). These data are generally inter-

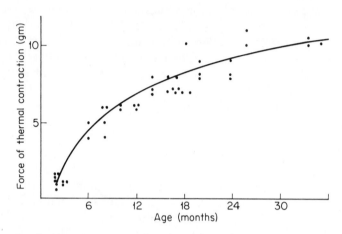

Fig. 3.8 Weight required to inhibit thermal contraction of rat tail tendon as a function of age. (Redrawn from Verzár. 1956. Experientia Suppl. IV. Birkhäuser Verlag, Basel.)

preted as indicating an increased cross linking. As might be anticipated, the most rapid rate of change takes place during growth, but change at slower rates occurs throughout the lifespan.

Other studies have been based on a phenomenon well-known to polymer chemists: that highly cross-linked polymers will imbibe water and swell under certain conditions. One form of swelling is the so-called osmotic, or Donnan equilibrium, type. Such swelling occurs maximally at certain pH levels. In the case of collagen in HCl solutions, H+ and Cl− ions diffuse into the tissue, where H+ ions neutralize carboxyl ions in the protein. At pH 2.5 there is a Donnan equilibrium established such that there is a maximal excess of diffusible Cl− ions inside the tissue over Cl− ions in the external medium. Ions inside will tend to diffuse out and will exert an osmotic pressure, causing the tissue to expand by separation of fibrils and subunits. In expanding, the tissue will imbibe water. The amount of swelling is actually a measure of the bulk modulus. Since swelling is restricted by stable cross links, the amount of swelling would be inversely related to the amount of such links.

Osmotic swelling at pH 2.5 probably involves only insoluble collagen, since tropocollagen and small aggregates would tend to be ex-

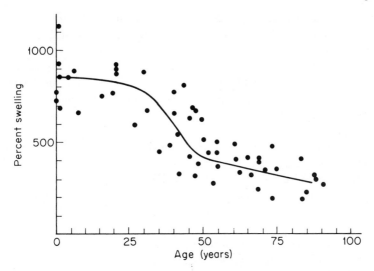

Fig. 3.9   Osmotic swelling of human tendon collagen as a function of age. (From Kohn and Rollerson. 1958. J. Gerontol. 13:241.)

tracted by the medium. Figure 3.9 shows swelling data for human tendon as a function of age. There is essentially no change before maturity. Between the ages of 30 and 50 years there is a rather abrupt decline in swelling ability. After 50 years of age, swelling ability continues to decrease at a slower rate.

Swelling of collagenous tissue is also caused by thermal denaturation below the temperature at which contraction occurs. This is probably due to an unfolding of coiled chains. With increasing age of tissues, there is an increase in the amount of time required for swelling and a decrease in extent of swelling. By combining thermal denaturation and osmotic swelling data for human tissue, four different stages of increasing cross linking can be identified as occurring over the life span.

A very large number of studies of aging collagen have been carried out with various tissues of different animals, utilizing different techniques. All properties of collagen that depend on cross linking or on degree of aggregation have been found to change with age in ways that would indicate greater cross linking. For example, old collagen is less susceptible to digestion by collagenase, is less easily gelatinized, and contains a smaller fraction that can be solubilized by hot extraction. Most of these studies have been undertaken with collagen-rich tissues such as skin, tendon, and bone.

In parenchymatous organs that contain smaller amounts of collagen and high concentrations of other substances, it is more difficult to gain information about aging collagen. However, Verzár's group and others have studied such collagen by determining solubility properties of hydroxyproline-rich fractions, and have obtained data indicating progressive cross linking with age.

All present data permit the conclusion that, following maturity, insoluble collagen throughout the body continues to undergo intermolecular cross linking, and that in human beings the most rapid and extensive cross linking occurs between the ages of approximately 30 and 50 years.

The types of bonds that form in aging collagen are not known. Most studies of collagen cross linking have been undertaken with soluble collagen. These have demonstrated some of the earliest cross links that form. Traditional analytical methods are applied to molecules in solution. Old collagen is one of the most insoluble of biological substances. In degrading it for analyses, it is very likely that age-related cross links would be ruptured or altered.

One possibility is that aging of collagen is caused by the same types of cross linking that form during maturation—that aging is a continuation of a developmental process. A number of different types of covalent bonds, as well as short-range forces associated with crystallization, have been described in maturing collagen. Ester links have been identified intramolecularly. However, attempts to rejuvenate old collagen by rupturing ester links with hydroxylamine have been unsuccessful. Similarly, bonds involving a pepsin-sensitive peptide have been implicated in maturation, but attempts to rejuvenate old collagen by pepsin treatment have failed. These negative data do not, of course, exclude the possibility that such bonds may be important in aging. They might be inaccessible to the agents employed, or additional bonds may mask the consequences of their rupture.

A second possibility is that the aggregation of subunits that occurs in maturation allows new types of specific aging bonds to form. In one of the few studies of cross linking in insoluble human collagen as a function of age, LaBella and Paul, working with acid hydrolysates described a decrease in tyrosine and an increase in a substance that fluoresces at 405 nm. The decrease in tyrosine, measured by fluorescence at 305 nm, and the increase in material fluorescing at 405 nm appear to occur linearly with age (Fig. 3.10). These workers suggest that tyrosine in collagen becomes oxidized to quinoids, which form covalent bonds with functional groups on adjacent molecules.

Finally, aging of collagen may be by rupture of some bonds that form during maturation, with the exposure of functional groups which can then form new types of bonds. Since our knowledge of cross linking during maturation is very incomplete, and we know even less about bonds forming with age, this possibility cannot be argued very extensively. However, there are some theoretical reasons for not rejecting

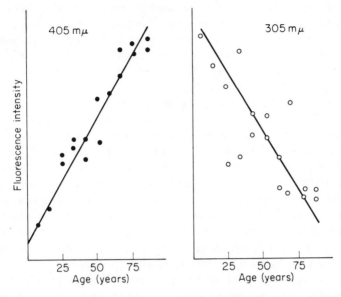

Fig. 3.10 Fluorescence intensity of human tendon at 305 nm (tyrosine) and 405 nm (presumed cross link) as a function of age. (Redrawn from LaBella and Paul. 1965. J. Gerontol. 20:54.)

such a mechanism. It has been pointed out that proteins that do not turn over are incubated at body temperature, 37–38°C, for many decades in the case of human beings. Such prolonged incubation would be expected to result in denaturation. It follows that if 37°C could cause denaturation over thirty or forty years, higher temperatures should cause the same type of denaturation in vitro over a short time interval.

Samples of human collagen were heated at 56°C for various periods, and their osmotic swelling ability was then determined. Elevated temperature caused collagen to show agelike changes in swelling capacity. Furthermore, by measuring rate of change at 56°C, using the energy of activation for thermal denaturation of collagen, and applying the Arrhenius equation, the length of time required at 37°C for loss of osmotic swelling ability, if such loss were due to thermal denaturation, could be calculated. Values obtained were from about 9 to 109 years and, in view of the extrapolations required, were considered consistent with the view that collagen aging could be caused by thermal denaturation. However, thermal denaturation at 56°C did not reproduce the age-related change in susceptibility to digestion by collagenase. Therefore, denaturation cannot be invoked as the sole cause of aging. It is possible that denaturation plays a role in causing rupture of some bonds with an altered molecular configuration, but that additional factors, formation of new bonds for example, are required for all of the manifestations of natural aging. Although it is difficult to conceive of no denaturation occurring with decades of incubation, we cannot decide on the basis of current information if such a process is of any importance in the aging of collagen.

Cross linking of collagen has been described as a physical-chemical process, which would appear to depend only on concentration, time, and temperature. Evidence in support of this view was obtained by experiments in which purified soluble collagen incubated for long periods in vitro, gave rise to mature insoluble collagen fibrils. No enzyme system or extraneous agents appeared to be required. However, some recent studies of collagen defects caused by the administration of certain nitriles to animals suggest that an amine oxidase may be required for normal cross linking in vivo. This fits with data showing that a cross link involving aldehyde groups from the oxidative deamination of lysine may form in maturing collagen.

It is also known that all of the age-related changes in collagen can be reproduced by treatment with a tanning agent, or cross linker, such as formaldehyde. Since the mammalian body contains many aldehydes that can function as cross linking agents, some workers have postulated that aging is caused by a generalized tanning of collagen and other proteins by extraneous small molecules. This seems a reasonable suggestion, and if such tanning does not occur, an explanation for its absence must be sought. It can only be stated that cross linking in vitro does not depend on such an agent, and that extensive analyses of collagen have not revealed the participation of such extraneous small molecules in cross linking. It may be that functional groups of collagen molecules and polypeptide chains form cross links before small molecules have a chance to participate, or that steric relationships exclude molecules from cross linking sites.

Extrinsic factors in collagen cross linking must be considered because of certain questions arising from comparative aspects of animal life span and rate of change in collagen. The rat lives about two and a half years, and its collagen becomes progressively cross linked. Human beings live 70 or more years and also show a progressive cross linking of collagen. If cross linking depends only on time and temperature, it is not clear why the oldest rat collagen should be any more cross linked than infantile human collagen. Because of different methods of measurement in different studies, it is not known if collagen at a given site in a 2½-year-old rat is cross linked to the same extent as that in a 70-year-old human being. However, on the basis of solubility data, the old rat collagen would appear to be much more densely cross linked than that of a 2½-year-old human. If old rat collagen and human collagen are cross linked to a similar degree, such cross linking may depend in part on metabolic factors. Smaller animals with shorter life spans have higher metabolic rates than larger animals with long life spans. A higher metabolic rate may result in the more rapid synthesis of enzymes or tanning agents which accelerate cross linking, although, as noted above, no requirement for these has been proven.

A role for metabolism in collagen cross linking has been suggested by the work of Rigby. He subjected collagen fibers to periodic stresses in vitro and found that X-ray diffraction patterns and physical measurements indicated that they were more crystalline and appeared more cross linked. Animals with higher metabolic rates have greater frequencies of tissue stresses. Such stresses might cause accelerated rates of cross linking in short-lived mammals. It is well-known, incidentally, that tensile stress facilitates the formation of crystalline regions in synthetic polymers, presumably by bringing charged and functional groups close enough together for interactions to occur.

Aging of elastin

Examination of elastin in tissues reveals rather conspicuous changes with age, in that old elastin appears frayed, fragmented, more brittle, and more yellow in color. The concept has arisen that elastin suffers from wear and tear, and that some profound chemical changes must be occurring. But, because of the difficulty in obtaining pure undegraded elastin, there is considerable confusion about the nature of such changes.

Early analytic studies indicated that aging of elastin was associated with a change in amino acid composition. Old elastin, thought to be reasonably pure, was found to contain increased amounts of dicarboxylic amino acids. However, from recent studies it can be concluded that the amino acid composition does not change, and that the dicarboxylic acids are from contamination by collagen, which as it ages becomes as insoluble as elastin.

As elastin ages it is found to contain more calcium salts, as noted earlier. This may represent simply a progressive deposition of minerals on elastin, or there may be an age-related molecular change in elastin which increases mineral binding. The latter possibility is suggested by studies in which human aortic elastin of various ages was incubated with calcium salts. An age-dependent increase in mineral binding was observed (Fig. 3.11). However, since the question of elastin purity has not been resolved, the possibility remains that calcium content and binding capacity may depend on contaminating collagen or polysaccharide.

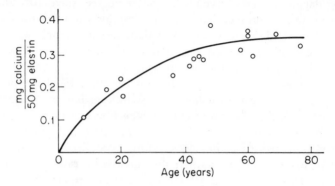

Fig. 3.11   Calcium bound in vitro by elastin from human aortas of different ages. (Redrawn from Eisenstein, et al. 1964. Lab. Invest. **13:**1198. Courtesy of International Academy of Pathology.)

An increased cross linking would be anticipated on the basis of experience with collagen. The two amino acids involved in cross linking, desmosine and isodesmosine, have been shown to increase in maturation of elastin, but appear to remain constant during aging. Another molecule involved in elastin cross links has been identified as lysinonorleucine, and is believed to form by the deamination of an ε-amino group of lysine, followed by a Schiff base formation between the resulting aldehyde group and another ε-amino group in a lysine residue on an adjacent chain. One study has indicated that this cross link increases with age.

One of the most prominent changes in elastin is what could be interpreted as signs of wear and tear. As noted above, elastin fibers in old blood vessels appear frayed, split, and fragmented (Fig. 3.12). We do not know if these changes are due simply to prolonged mechanical damage or to chemical changes, or whether chemical changes occur which facilitate mechanical damage.

Some generalities

Although there are large gaps in our knowledge, we have enough information to provide us with some general impressions about aging of the extracellular compartment. There appears to be some loss of acid mucopolysaccharide, and changes in relative amounts of some types of polysaccharide. These may cause less water-binding in tissues and a redistribution of water. Collagen, the major fibrous protein, becomes progressively cross linked. Similar changes probably occur in elastin. The latter appears damaged and less elastic. There

Fig. 3.12 Human iliac arteries stained for elastin. Reduced slightly from ×90. Top, 18-year-old artery, showing wavy lamellae. Bottom, 58-year-old artery, showing fragmentation of elastin. (From Blumenthal, et al. 1950. Am. J. Path. **26**:989.)

is an accumulation of calcium salts, lipids, and possibly other materials in or on extracellular components.

We have not considered the significance or consequences of these age-changes. Consequences will be apparent only when we ask specific questions based on aging at higher levels of organization. That is, key aging processes occur at the level of molecules, but we cannot appreciate their significance until we ask questions about aging at the level of cell, organ, or intact animal. We shall return to aging of extracellular components in attempting to explain aging at higher levels.

Major questions for future work

1. Mucopolysaccharide content and turnover. Much more information is required about the effect of age on the concentration of various polysaccharides and their turnover rates, particularly in parenchymatous organs. Although some data are available on turnover, the rate of turnover has received little attention as a function of age; it is of interest because differences in turnover rate have been invoked to explain differences in concentration. Age-changes in polysaccharides may be of great significance in tissue hydration and in physiologic processes.

2. Water distribution. Loss of hyaluronic acid and cross linking of proteins would be expected to result in a redistribution of water so that, instead of being uniformly distributed through the connective tissue, the tissue would be compartmentalized into water-rich and water-poor phases. Such a change would be important in physiologic processes, but this possibility has not been adequately investigated. Studies of hydration by such techniques as interference microscopy and by the isolation of hydrated components would be useful.

3. Basement membranes. Essentially nothing is known about aging of these structures, other than that they have been reported to thicken. Because they are in key positions to regulate the passage of materials, any age-related change would be likely to cause alteration in diffusion processes. Ultrastructural studies might reveal morphological, organizational, or chemical changes, and might be used to discover differences in transport of certain particles.

4. Accumulation of materials. Most studies dealing with this question have been carried out with blood vessels. Connective tissue of parenchymatous organs should be analyzed to discover if minerals, lipids, and glycoproteins accumulate with age. Fractionation of tissue to remove cells might be accomplished with the aid of enzymes which degrade cellular components.

5. Cross linking of proteins. The chemical nature of collagen cross links must be determined, and it must be ascertained whether or not progressive cross linking occurs in elastin. This will involve sophisticated methods of purifying and degrading these proteins, techniques of organic analysis, and possibly nondestructive analytical procedures.

6. Cross linking in different animals. Identical methods applied to collagen at a given site in old short-lived and old long-lived animals should indicate whether the two collagens are cross linked to the same extent. Additional studies of the role of enzymes, tanning agents, and stresses in cross linking of collagen are required in order to explain probable differences in rates of cross linking.

REFERENCES

Butzow, J. W. and G. L. Eichhorn. 1968. Physical chemical studies on the age changes in rat tail tendon collagen. Biochim. Biophys. Acta. 154:208.

Gross, J. 1961. Ageing of connective tissue; the extracellular components. In G. H. Bourne [ed.] Structural aspects of aging. Hafner Publ. Co., New York.

Kohn, R. R. and E. J. Rollerson. 1959. Studies on the effect of heat and age in decreasing ability of human collagen to swell in acid. J. Gerontol. **14:**11.

LaBella, F. S. and W. G. Lindsay. 1963. The structure of human aortic elastin as influenced by age. J. Gerontol. **18:**111.

Piez, K. A. 1968. Cross-linking of collagen and elastin. Ann. Rev. Biochem. **37:**547.

Rigby, B. J. 1964. Effect of cyclic extension on the physical properties of tendon collagen and its possible relation to biological ageing of collagen. Nature. **202:**1072.

Schaub, M. C. 1963. Qualitative and quantitative changes of collagen in parenchymatous organs of the rat during aging. Gerontologia. **8:**114.

Seifter, S. and P. M. Gallop. 1966. The structure proteins. In H. Neurath [ed.] The proteins. Academic Press, New York.

Sobel, H. 1967. Aging of ground substance in connective tissue. Adv. in Gerontol. Res. **2:**205.

Walford, R. L., P. K. Carter, and R. B. Schneider. 1964. Stability of labeled aortic elastic tissue with age and pregnancy in the rat. Arch. Pathol. **78:**43.

FOUR

Intracellular Aging

In considering the aging of intracellular components, we are immediately faced with problems of categorizing information and acquiring frames of reference. We shall be interested in components that turn over in stable cells, and in cells that are themselves turning over, as well as in nonrenewable materials in both stable and turning-over cells. Interpretation of data is further complicated by such factors as growth and function, which may cause or reverse certain alterations. In this chapter we shall consider aging of intracellular components as an extension of chemical aging. That is, we shall discuss those changes occurring inside of cells which appear to satisfy the criteria of aging processes, in starting or accelerating at maturity and in being progressive and irreversible. At this point we shall not deal extensively with the types of cells in which these changes are occurring. The significance of aging of intracellular components in different kinds of cells will be considered in the next chapter.

Aging of components which turn over

When radioisotopes were first used widely as tracers in metabolic studies, the impression was gained that most proteins and organelles were in a dynamic state. It appeared that these substances and structures throughout the mammalian body were being continuously synthesized and degraded or lost, many at very rapid rates. When some of these systems were studied in more detail, however, it was found that many turnover rates did not reflect synthesis and degradation of intracellular components. In some cases what had been measured was turnover of entire cells rather than their constituents. Proteins in cells of the gastrointestinal tract appear to have a high rate of turnover because the cells that contain them are continuously being shed and replaced. Periodic sampling of the mucosa for determination of isotope content would not reveal the basis of protein turnover. Some organs such as liver produce large amounts of protein that leave the cells and are utilized elsewhere. Many serum proteins, for example, are produced in the liver. Since these are released from cells shortly after synthesis, analyses of pooled liver cell proteins would give erroneous high values for protein turnover. Furthermore, certain assumptions about protein pools have been found untenable. A fraction of myosin, the major structural protein of muscle, can be extracted in high ionic strength buffers. Isotope incorporation into this fraction indicated that myosin turned over quite rapidly. However, this fraction of myosin is probably not representative of the total myosin, and appears to exist in a pool that is metabolically different from that of the less easily extracted myosin. At present we do not know the turnover rate of this important protein.

Although the question of turnover requires extensive reexamination, certain conclusions are justified on the basis of current information. All of the soluble enzymes and other soluble proteins such as those in serum turn over continuously. Turnover rates for these molecules are quite high. Times required for one-half of the molecules to disappear and be replaced by newly synthesized molecules usually vary between several hours and several weeks, depending on the protein. Half-lives of some soluble enzymes are measured in hours, or less; the half-life of liver tyrosine transaminase, for example, being about 1.5 hours. In some cases there appear to be feedback mechanisms working to control synthetic and degradative processes. When one accelerates or slows down, the other does likewise in apparent attempts to maintain constant protein concentrations.

Insoluble or structural proteins turn over at slower rates, and some may be metabolically inert. These are the proteins we know least about. Proteolipid protein of the central nervous system is not turned over, and this may be typical of proteins in structures such as cell membranes and nerve sheaths. The turnover of histones, the basic proteins associated with DNA, has not been studied very extensively. However, the few studies available suggest that different fractions of histone turn over at different rates, that turnover of some fractions may accompany RNA synthesis, and that there is considerable variation between different organs in rates of turnover.

Although DNA is synthesized in populations of dividing cells, once formed, it is not degraded. Such complex molecules, just sitting there, as it were, for prolonged periods would be likely candidates for age-changes. RNA, on the other hand, exists in a number of different populations, some of which have half-lives measured in hours or less.

Turnover of organelles appears to be quite rapid, and may have little or no relationship to the division of cells that contain them. Liver mitochondria have a half-life of around 10 days, which indicates that they are turning over within cells that are not dividing. Since different components of the mitochondria have approximately the same turnover rates, it has been concluded that these organelles are synthesized and degraded as units. The half-life of microsomal proteins has been determined from in vitro studies of rat liver to be slightly over a day.

Thus, many cell components, notably the soluble proteins and organelles, demonstrate rather high rates of turnover which appear to represent programmed, or normal, ongoing metabolic processes. The possible role of aging in these processes has generally not been appreciated, and experimental work bearing on this question has not been undertaken. We may, however, postulate that aging processes are of significance in normal turnover. The question is whether or not populations of molecules and organelles undergo progressive changes before they are degraded. A related question is: Do degradative enzymes recognize age-altered molecules and structures and selectively degrade them as they are replaced by young, newly synthesized populations?

The fact that we describe turnover rates in terms of half-lives denotes that loss of molecules is a logarithmic function or a random-hit process in which there is no selection of the molecules that are lost. Exponential die-away curves have been obtained for several highly purified molecules and organelles. Frequently, however, the curves appear to represent composites of fast and slow reactions, some of which may be first-order. An exponential curve could be obtained for the loss of aged molecules if the rate of aging were very fast compared to the rate of loss or degradation—that is, if they were aged in the sense of being unstable shortly after synthesis. The population of aged molecules would then be a large percentage of the total molecules, and their loss could be first-order.

A number of unrelated observations suggest that aging may play a role in turnover. If a solution of protein molecules or a suspension of organelles such as mitochondria or microsomes is maintained under physiological conditions of pH, ionic strength, and temperature, the populations invariably deteriorate. In the case of proteins, the deterioration is in the form of denaturation with loss of enzyme activities. Some proteins may be kept at equilibrium indefinitely under special conditions of pH and ionic environment, but such conditions would not be likely to persist for long in vivo. Organelles similarly show a loss in biological activity, associated with protein denaturation, and loss of morphological integrity manifested by fragmentation and vacuolization. It has long been known that denatured proteins are more susceptible to degradation by proteolytic enzymes than are native proteins. A useful hypothesis might be that complex molecules and organelles do age, primarily by denaturation, and that age-altered molecules are selectively degraded in the course of normal turnover. Indeed, if such aging and degradation were found not to occur, additional mechanisms would have to be invoked to explain their prevention.

Teleological reasoning also tends to support this notion. If intracellular components did not become altered with time, there would be no obvious reason for turnover to take place. A complement of enzymes and organelles, once synthesized, would remain present indefinitely, carrying out their functions. One can argue the possibility that turnover mechanisms evolved to circumvent the consequences of aging of certain labile intracellular components. It could also be argued teleologically that turnover occurs so concentrations of components can vary in response to varying functional demands. These questions are amenable to experimental studies, and should constitute a fruitful area for investigation.

Previous studies on the aging of dynamic intracellular components have been hindered by at least two major obstacles. The first is that it has not been feasible to follow properties of a given population of molecules or organelles over their life spans. In most cases the life spans were not known. As an example, comparisons have been made between mitochondria from liver and brain of young and old rats. Since mitochondria appear to turn over in liver with a half-life of 10–12 days, it is most likely that mitochondria in liver from both old and young animals are approximately the same age, but may be in quite different environments. And since almost nothing is known about turnover of brain mitochondria, it cannot be decided if any age-related differences observed are manifestations of intrinsic mitochondrial aging, of age-related differences in turnover, or of an altered metabolic or physiologic environment.

The second major problem is in the interpretation of observations of age-related changes in both concentration and structure of turning over components. These components are exceedingly labile and responsive to physiological changes. The concentration of pancreatic enzymes changes rapidly in response to food intake. Animals which have undergone physical training show increased concentrations of lactate dehydrogenase in heart and decreases in skeletal muscle. Similarly, exercise may cause an increase of up to 80 percent in muscle myoglobin. Rapid variations in enzyme concentration during development and in response to hormones and vitamins have been frequently documented. Such lability would be assumed to extend to the protein-synthesizing machinery, where it would be manifested by changes in

RNA, microsomes, and endoplasmic reticulum. Relatively short periods of exercise cause a marked increase in the size of heart mitochondria, whereas cold acclimatization causes increased fragility of liver mitochondria.

Such subcellular alterations in response to changing functional demands, presumably associated with a variety of feedback mechanisms, are of great interest and constitute major challenges in biology. However, they tend to confuse the picture when questions dealing with aging are asked. As will be discussed in later sections, aging animals show many debilities. We shall try to describe underlying causes for these debilities. Whatever the causes might be, in the presence of altered function we would expect many changes in dynamic intracellular components. In other words, we may not be able to distinguish cause from effect; age-related changes observed in components that turn over may not represent fundamental aging of these components, but, rather, trivial consequences of age-changes at higher levels of organization.

The question posed in this section was whether or not components that normally turn over demonstrate aging changes before loss or degradation. It must be concluded that although a priori reasoning suggests that such aging does occur, more direct experimental data are required. We can now consider aging of dynamic intracellular components in aging cells and organisms.

Long-term changes in renewable intracellular components

Changes would not be anticipated over long periods of time in the structure or function of individual molecules or organelles that are turning over rapidly. Any truly intrinsic changes observed would be most readily explained on the basis of age-related alterations in rates of synthesis or degradation such that older cells, for example, turned over components at slower rates so that altered molecules or organelles accumulated. Alternatively, altered molecules could be explained on the basis of accumulation of mutations with time. No qualitative age-changes in renewable soluble proteins have been described, nor have they been sought with any enthusiasm. Early ultrastructural studies described mitochondria of cells from older animals as showing fragmentation. Similar fragmentation was described in the golgi apparatus, as was a loss of chromidial substance in neurones. More recent data suggest that such changes may have been due to physiological differences between young and old animals or to variations in susceptibility to damage by procedures used. The latter could represent an intrinsic age difference, and requires more study.

Studies of the ultrastructure of cardiac muscle and autonomic ganglion cells from young and old rats have revealed no differences in mitochondria, sarcoplasmic reticulum, or golgi apparatus. As shown in Fig. 4.1, the morphology of mitochondria and myofibrils is remarkably

Fig. 4.1 Cardiac muscle from 90-day-old rat (top) and 1004-day-old rat (bottom). Reduced slightly from ×21,000. (From Sulkin and Sulkin. 1967. J. Gerontol. 22: 485.)

similar in rats of very different ages. When young and old animals were exposed to low oxygen tension for long periods, mitochondria from old rats were much more severely affected. They became swollen and fragmented, while mitochondria from young animals showed little change (Fig. 4.2). Mitochondria of autonomic ganglion cells from old animals also showed marked swelling with loss of cristae and matrix as a response to low oxygen tension, while the organelles from young animals were relatively unaffected. These studies support the view that qualitative changes in dynamic components over long periods may

Fig. 4.2 Cardiac muscle from 118-day-old rat (top) and 1032-day-old rat (bottom) after 28 days in 5.5% O₂ chamber. Reduced slightly from ×32,600. (From Sulkin and Sulkin. 1967. J. Gerontol. 22:485.)

represent more the effects of environment than of intrinsic aging. In other words, old debilitated animals cannot handle stresses for reasons that will be suggested in later sections, and this continuing inadequacy, or borderline function, may result in subcellular alterations.

A more direct approach to the study of dynamic cellular constituents is to measure their functional capacities in vitro. Metabolic reactions are generally the function of soluble enzymes and organelles that demonstrate rapid turnover, and these reactions can be measured in the laboratory. Some reservations in interpretation are required because, as noted above, the amount and state of these components may reflect the recent history of animals from which they are obtained.

Homogenates of rat brain and liver have been found to show no age-related variation in oxygen consumption. Nor have changes with age been observed in oxidative phosphorylation in brain homogenates and in glycolytic phosphorylation. Succinoxidase activity is approximately the same in mitochondria from young and old rat kidney. Similarly, oxidative phosphorylation of mitochondria from rat liver, heart, and kidney has been reported not to change with age. Rat liver mitochondria, in a more detailed study, showed no change in oxidative phosphorylation (P/O ratio) as a function of age when α-ketoglutarate, malate, and succinate were used as substrates. However, with β-hydroxybutarate as substrate, a significant decline with age in phosphorylation with a constant P/O ratio was described. This suggests some structural age-related change in mitochondria whose cause and significance cannot be evaluated without additional data. Mitochondria from aged animals have also been shown to be more sensitive to such treatments as freezing and thawing, incubation at 37°C, and to a toxic agent.

It can be concluded at this point that when renewable components are examined over long periods, very little in the way of qualitative changes can be detected. Those which have been described might be due to extrinsic causes. It should be noted that we have been discussing properties of renewable cell components and have not considered concentration changes, or changes in dynamic components in short-lived cells that are themselves aging or dying. In addition, a very large number of renewable macromolecules have not been studied in terms of changes in structure or activity as a function of age.

Long-term quantitative changes in renewable components

The amount of a soluble enzyme that is present or the concentration of organelles within a tissue is usually determined by sampling the tissue, preparing a fraction that contains the substance in question, and determining the amount of activity present by chemical methods. In most studies of this type, activity is used as a measure of quantity, although no information is obtained on inactive or masked enzymes present or on the presence of inhibitors. Also, the nutritional or physiological state of the animal is frequently overlooked. Growing and active animals generally have tissues with higher metabolic rates, higher concentrations of enzymes, and faster protein synthesis than mature animals. Thus, tissues from young animals differ significantly from those of old animals in terms of these components. Adhering to earlier definitions, we are interested in differences between mature and old animals rather than between old and young. Or at the level of cells, we shall be concerned more with differences between mature or differentiated cells and old cells than with variations between rapidly dividing stem cells and differentiated cells.

The only way a population of molecules can change quantitatively is by a change in the rate at which the molecules are synthesized or degraded. Rates of protein synthesis have been of great theoretical interest in aging. It has frequently been postulated that defects accumulate in DNA or in translation or transcription, and that inadequate protein synthesis is a major cause of both cell and animal aging. Before attempting to evaluate the role of such defects in aging at higher levels of organization, as will be done in later chapters, it is necessary to determine if, in fact, there are alterations in protein synthesis or degradation associated with aging. Because of the extreme lability of enzyme and organelle concentration with variation in function, the capacity or potential of a cell to synthesize or degrade a constituent when stimulated is probably of more significance than the amount of that constituent which might be determined at any instant.

Barrows and Roeder determined the concentrations of a variety of enzymes in liver, kidney, and heart of young, mature, and old rats. The most striking differences were between immature and adult animals. No significant differences in enzyme per cell were found with aging between 12 and 24 months of age, except for an increase in the case of cathepsin. These workers also depleted the level of enzymes in animals of different ages by a protein-deficient diet and then determined how fast the enzymes could be synthesized when the rats were given adequate diets. They found no age-related differences in rate of protein synthesis, and concluded that the evidence did not favor impairment in protein synthesis with aging. This conclusion was supported by subsequent studies of lactate dehydrogenase and malate dehydrogenase in five rat organs. Between the ages of 12 and 24 months, the only change was an equivocal decline in skeletal muscle lactate dehydrogenase (Fig. 4.3). Additional studies of the rat central nervous

Fig. 4.3 Effect of age on lactic dehydrogenase activity of various tissues of rats. (From Schmuckler and Barrows. 1966. J. Gerontol. **21:**109.)

	Age (months)			
Tissue	*1*	*3*	*12*	*24*
Liver	170.2± 9.5 [a]	150.4± 8.1	163.7±13.6	173.9± 8.5
Kidney	120.3± 3.9	129.6± 5.8	125.1± 7.2	122.9± 5.5
Brain	126.1± 8.4	120.5± 9.4	113.7± 5.9	113.6± 4.0
Muscle	255.6±11.8	324 ±18.7	344.7±18.2	284.2±13.7
Heart	229.6±15.2	280.8±13.4	288.3± 9.5	273.9±10.8

[a] Moles DPN per Gm. protein/hr. $\times 10^{-3} \pm SE_M$.

system and the human aorta have also failed to support the view that the synthesis of intracellular protein is impaired with age.

Contradictory results have been obtained in other studies. Lactate dehydrogenase has been found to increase during growth of rats, and then to decline significantly in skeletal muscle and heart with age, while showing equivocal changes in brain and liver (Fig. 4.4). Fumarase activity has been reported to remain constant during adult life in mouse intestinal mucosa and liver, while declining in diaphragm and kidney. Also in mice, a decrease with age in phosphomonoesterase activity of intestinal mucosa has been demonstrated.

Thus, studies based on sampling of tissues and determining contents of enzyme activity have revealed no pattern of change with age. Some enzymes have been found to remain constant while others decrease, and conflicting results have been obtained. Because of the extreme lability of enzyme concentration, best appreciated by changes during growth, one wonders if some of the reported changes with age and conflicting observations are due to differences in diets or to the physiological state of the animals.

Several additional investigations have dealt directly with the ability to synthesize protein as a function of age. The hormone dexamethasone causes increases in several liver enzymes. When this agent was given to rats of various ages, an age-related decline in amount of induced enzyme was observed (Fig. 4.5). It will be noted that these studies were taken out only to 15 months of age. Rats live $2\frac{1}{2}$ to 3 years and are still growing at a significant rate at 15 months. In fact, the rate of decline in induced enzyme level appears to be rather closely related to changes in the growth rate. The most rapid loss was immediately after weaning, when the rats were growing most rapidly. Relationships between growth and aging will be discussed in a later chapter. However, it will be sufficient for the present and in the light of earlier definitions of aging to ask whether or not data of Fig. 4.5 represent an aging system. With reference to aging of the intact animal, such a change in induced enzyme is clearly not an aging process, because it slows with maturation rather than beginning or accelerating at this time. The question cannot be answered with reference to cell aging, because it is not known if loss of inducibility of the enzyme is a function of the age of cells. Liver cells turn over, and turnover rates may vary with rates of growth. A liver, then, contains cells of different ages, and the age distribution of the populations may be different in animals of different ages.

Gutmann and co-workers studied protein synthesis in nerves following nerve section and observed that 24 to 28-month-old rats did not contain as much newly synthesized protein as 1 to 3-month-old rats. Since the young rats were growing rapidly, this information is not very

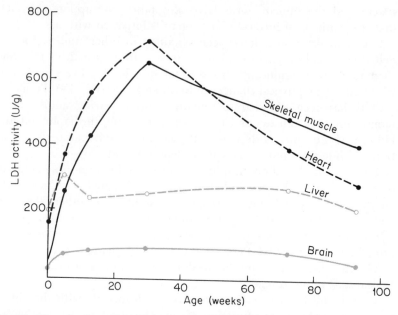

Fig. 4.4 Effect of age on lactic dehydrogenase activity of various tissues of rats. (Drawn from data of Singh and Kanungo. 1968. J. Biol. Chem. **243:**4526. Used with permission of copyright holder, The American Society of Biological Chemists.)

Fig. 4.5 Dexamethasone-induced synthesis of hepatic fructose-1, 6-diphosphatase in rats of different ages. (From Singhal. 1967. J. Gerontol. **22:**77.)

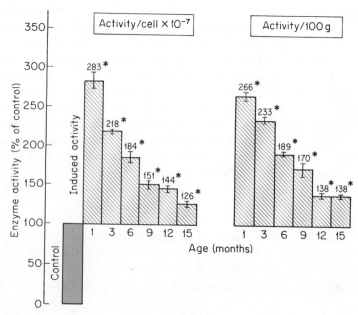

useful with regard to animal aging for the reasons noted above. A comparison between 12- and 24-month-old animals would be more meaningful. However, since nerve cells do not turn over, this can probably be accepted as an example of intracellular aging. Questions posed by this study are 1) To what extent is metabolism of long-lived stable cells such as neurones influenced by extrinsic factors depending on the age of the animal which contains them? 2) When a smaller amount of protein is identified at a given time, does this result from decreased synthesis or increased degradation?

Additional informative studies of the capacity to synthesize proteins have been carried out with relatively mature and old rats. The liver enzyme tryptophan peroxidase is an adaptive enzyme, in that its synthesis is stimulated by the presence of substrate. Also, both this enzyme and tyrosine transaminase are increased in response to adrenal hormone treatment. When 12- to 13-month-old rats and 24- to 26-month-old rats were treated with enzyme substrate and with the hormone, their livers showed marked increases in enzyme content, and there were no age-related differences (Fig. 4.6). Nor were significant age-related

Age, mo.	Tryptophan Peroxidase			Tyrosine Transaminase	
	Basal	After tyrptophan	After hydrocortisone	Basal	After hydrocortisone
12–13	11.1±0.9 (12)	70.4±2.3 (12)	35.6±1.7 (13)	103±10 (12)	338±38 (13)
24–26	12.7±1.1 (12)	71.4±5.7 (12)	35.1±2.5 (13)	96±12 (12)	423±36 (13)

Activities are given as means and their S.E. Numbers in parentheses indicate number of animals in each group. Activities are expressed as µmoles of enzyme product formed per gram dry weight of liver per hour. None of the differences between groups is statistically significant.

Fig. 4.6 Tryptophan peroxidase and tyrosine transaminase after stimulation in mature and old rats. (From Gregerman. 1959. Am. J. Physiol. 197:63.)

differences observed in basal concentrations of the enzymes. Gregerman argues that this lack of an age-related difference in protein synthesis, stimulated by two methods, is strong evidence against the view that there is a decline in ability to synthesize protein associated with aging.

Finally, the induction of the liver enzyme tryptophan pyrrolase by injection of tryptophan has been studied in rats of different ages. There was no difference in rate of synthesis between the ages of 3 and 12 months, although weaning rats of one month showed a differently shaped curve for enzyme induction (Fig. 4.7).

Fig. 4.7 Induction of rat liver tryptophan pyrrolase as a function of age. Age in months indicated for each curve. (Redrawn from Correl, et al. 1965. J. Gerontol. **20**:507.)

The proteins discussed in this section are within cells that have long life spans in relation to animal life spans. Nerve cells, heart and skeletal muscle cells do not normally divide or turn over, and are generally present and viable throughout the animal life span. Liver cells and, to a lesser extent, kidney cells have the capacity to divide, and may do so rapidly under certain circumstances. However, they normally have a very low rate of division and replacement. It appears clear that in these cells there is no widespread or generalized quantitative change in dynamic components associated with age. There also appears to be no significant or generalized loss of capacity to synthesize proteins in these long-lived cells, as a function of the age of the animal. It may be argued that there is suggestive evidence that some proteins are less rapidly synthesized with age, that some studies have shown lower enzyme concentrations, and that since only a small number of proteins have been studied, the possibility remains that there is a decline in the ability to synthesize certain key molecules that have not yet been studied. Perhaps, however, the burden of proof should be on the view that aging is associated with an inability to synthesize proteins. To represent an intrinsic aging change, such a decline in synthetic ability would have to accelerate after maturity of the system involved, and would have to occur independently of growth, activity, and systemic physiological alterations.

Aging of dynamic components in individual short-lived cells

Changes in neurones and in muscle cells occurring over the animal's life span should be considered examples of intracellular aging, since these cells do not normally divide and are not replaced. Investigations of tissues such as epithelia, liver, or kidney cannot properly be viewed as intracellular studies, because it is not known whether any changes noted occur within a given cell during its life span. Over very long periods, it is very likely that different cells are being studied as a result of cell turnover. Stable and very slowly turning over cells comprise the majority of cells in mammals.

There are many populations of cells in mammals, however, that have short life spans in relationship to the animal's life span. These cells are born and die quite independently of the animal which contains them. They appear to have rates of turnover that are rapid and programmed. Typically, there is a zone or focus where stem cells divide, giving rise to the cell population. The newly formed cells do not divide, but undergo chemical and morphological specialization. They then deteriorate and die. As they die, they are replaced by new cells. Examples of such cell populations are stratified epithelia of the skin and urinary tract, glandular epithelia of the gastrointestinal tract, red blood cells, and granulocytic leukocytes. Between the last cell division and death, each cell in these populations represents an aging system.

In many cases the entire cell life span can be observed in one microscopic field. In a stratified squamous epithelium, division occurs in the basal cell layer. In the superficial layers division does not occur, but the cells become flattened and synthesize large amounts of keratin. Dynamic cell populations usually synthesize some special product such as mucin, glycogen, enzymes, hemoglobin, or keratin. In the case of squamous epithelium we know that the basal cells synthesize little or no keratin, whereas the superficial cells synthesize large amounts. Because of this difference in synthesis and the marked changes in appearance with aging, we can assume that very profound changes occur with age in the enzyme complement of such cells. However, essentially no systematic work has been done on changing enzyme patterns in cells of this type with special reference to cell aging.

Some studies carried out on special populations of dynamic cells suggest that quantitative changes do occur in turning-over cell components, and also suggest an answer to the question posed earlier about the possibility that turning-over molecules become aged before they are lost or degraded. Rat neutrophils have life spans measured in hours, and they do not divide. When such cells are maintained in vitro, under what appear to be ideal conditions, there is a rapid loss in the activity of at least two enzymes, succinic dehydrogenase and an enzyme, or enzymes responsible for lactic acid production (Fig. 4.8). There are many possible explanations for this observation. However, it is likely that degradation, denaturation, or loss through diffusion proceeds faster than synthesis of enzymes, which may decrease with age in vitro.

Fig. 4.8   Properties of rat leukocytes aging in vitro. (From Kohn and Fitzgerald. 1964. Exptl. Molec. Pathol. 3:51.)

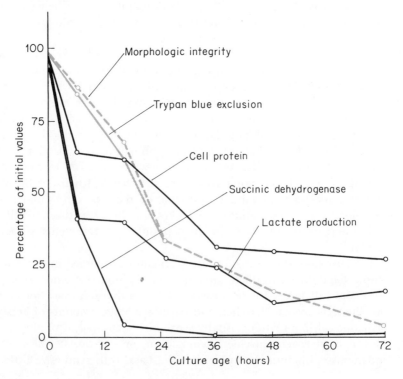

Red blood cells have received a lot of attention because of their use in medicine and because they can be isolated in large amounts. The mature cell in mammals has lost its nucleus and has a life span in the circulation of dogs and human beings of about 110 days. Without the nucleus, the cell cannot synthesize new messenger RNA, and protein synthesis is essentially cut off, although hypothetically some synthesis could occur because of persisting RNA. Thus, although the red cell is far from a typical cell, it is of use in the study of intracellular aging because aging processes are not complicated by growth and syntheses. In the absence of aging processes there would be no reason for the red cell's not remaining at equilibrium or in a steady state indefinitely.

Red cells can be obtained from an individual, and mature cells can be separated from old ones by utilizing specific gravity differences. A number of studies are in agreement that there is a generalized loss in the activity of many enzymes with cell aging, or after loss of nuclei. This would be anticipated, and is presumably on the basis of either enzyme denaturation or loss by diffusion. One enzyme, catalase, appears to be maintained at a constant level of activity with age. However, this enzyme exists in at least three forms and, with age, there is a decrease in one form and an increase in a second. This may represent molecular aggregation with age if the three catalases are isozymes formed by interactions of small numbers of subunits. A structural change with age has also been demonstrated in the β chain of hemoglobin which is manifested by alteration in electrical charge. In the normal nucleated cell such soluble proteins would probably be turning over, and changes of the type described would be very hard to detect. These data suggest that, in the absence or slowing of protein synthesis, losses or alterations in some proteins would be expected, and these could proceed to a point incompatible with cell life. The catalase and hemoglobin data also hint that soluble proteins in nucleated cells might be altered before being lost and replaced.

On the other hand, a study of mouse red blood cells aged in vivo, in which new cell formation was inhibited by actinomycin D treatment, showed no loss of glucose-6-phosphate dehydrogenase and 6-phosphogluconate dehydrogenase during 35 days. If this finding is confirmed, it would be a demonstration of remarkable enzyme stability.

The protein-synthesizing machinery and age

The most direct approach to the problem of protein synthesis as a function of age would be to study the macromolecules, organelles, and co-factors responsible for the synthesis of proteins. A number of such studies have been undertaken, frequently with the assumption that there is a generalized age-related decrease in the ability to synthesize proteins, even though this is a tenuous notion, as discussed above. Few studies have been carried out, unfortunately, on what happens within an individual cell with the passage of time, and most investigations of this type have been done with tissues obtained from animals of different ages.

The DNA content of bovine thymus and of rat brain, muscle, kidney, and liver cells does not change significantly over the animals' life spans. Histones, which have been measured only in bovine thymus, similarly remain constant in total concentration. It has been postulated by von Hahn that there is an increased binding of histones to DNA with age. He isolated fractions containing various histone-DNA aggregates from bovine thymus and found equivocal changes with age in concentrations of the fractions. Extending these studies to rat liver, von Hahn isolated fractions with similar histone/DNA concentration ratios from animals of different ages and determined their melting temperatures, on the assumption that melting temperature was a measure of the strength of DNA-histone binding. Although there was a marked scatter of values, results were consistent with the view that binding increased with age (Fig. 4.9).

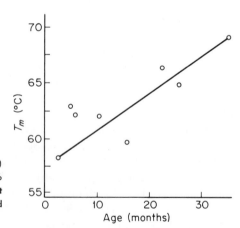

Fig. 4.9 Melting temperature (T_m) for DNA preparations with 1–2% histone from rat liver of different ages. (Redrawn from von Hahn and Fritz. 1966. *Gerontologia.* 12:237.)

At a higher level of organization, that of the chromosome, some interesting observations have been made. The unfertilized egg is a useful example of an aging cell. It has been observed that chromosomes of aging rabbit eggs become pycnotic or scattered. Also, increased numbers of aneuploid lymphocytes in human females and lymphocytes lacking Y chromosomes in males have been reported in the aged.

The question of age and abnormal chromosomes has also been studied by Curtis, who treated mice with an agent to destroy much of the liver and then scored gross chromosomal aberrations in dividing cells as a function of age in liver as it regenerated. He found that the percentage of aberrations increased with age, that the increase was greater in a short-lived mouse strain, and that irradiation caused a marked increase in the percentage of altered cells. With the passage of time after irradiation, there was a drop in the percentage of aberrations (Fig. 4.10). The significance of these observations will be dis-

Fig. 4.10 Chromosomal aberrations as a function of age of short- (A/HEJ) and long- (C57BL)-lived strains of mice, and of mice following irradiation. (Redrawn from data of Curtis. 1963. Science. 141:686. Copyright 1963 by the American Association for the Advancement of Science.)

cussed in later sections dealing with the aging of animals. However, for the time being, it should be noted that the long-lived strain apparently never has as many aberrations as the short-lived strain has at the end of its median life span, that the rate of increase either slows or stops after about one year of age, that the short-lived strain has about as many abnormal chromosomes at about 250 days of age as the long-lived strain has at the end of its life span, that irradiated animals at 4 months of age have close to twice as many altered chromosomes as the long-lived mice at the ends of their life spans, and that aberrations do not increase after maturity.

The activity of liver DNA polymerase has been found to decrease with age when two-stranded DNA was used as primer, but to increase with heat-denatured DNA. However, this change is clearly correlated with growth rate rather than aging, because the most rapid rate of change is in young growing animals. The change is also reversible, in that regenerating liver polymerase takes on the properties of the enzyme from young liver.

It has been reported that nuclear RNA is synthesized more rapidly in old than in very young rat liver. The most obvious interpretation would be that this component of the protein-synthesizing process becomes more efficient with age. However, another study comparing mature and old livers indicated a decreased rate of synthesis of nuclear RNA with age, as well as changes in base composition. The small amount of information on RNA is thus contradictory, and more studies are required.

It appears that at the chromosome level, gross alterations occur in the aging of short-lived cells—at least in eggs, and probably in the aging of organs such as liver. At the molecular level, however, we must draw the same conclusions as from the studies of protein synthesis. No intrinsic age-related defect in function of the protein-synthesizing machinery has been consistently demonstrated.

Degradation of intracellular components

When one is considering how intracellular components might be broken down or gotten rid of, the major problem would appear to be removal of macromolecules and structural complexes. Smaller molecules might diffuse out of cells, or participate, or be consumed in a variety of metabolic reactions. Mechanisms by which complex molecules might be degraded bear on problems of aging in several ways. In the normal turnover of macromolecules, discussed earlier as possibly representing aging of a population, synthesis rates must be balanced by degradative rates in order to maintain a stable population size. If rate of degradation exceeded or was exceeded by rate of synthesis, the population would diminish or become larger. Any progressive and irreversible change in population size would represent an aging process. Thus, degradative processes could play a role in the aging of a population of molecules of constant size, or could determine concentration changes with age.

If synthesis or accumulation of molecules occurs and there is no mechanism of degradation, the result will be an accumulation of molecules—an aging process. Similarly, if synthesis subsides and degradation does not occur, the result will be a stable population of molecules which could then undergo such age-changes as denaturation, polymerization or crystallization.

As animals age there is frequently a wasting or atrophy of organs. A good example of this is skeletal muscle atrophy, which is probably secondary to generalized debility and lack of function rather than due to intrinsic cellular aging processes. Such consequences of aging are associated with losses of large amounts of structural proteins, enzymes, and organelles. The end point of cell aging is cell death. In some cases, particularly when such cells are at epithelial surfaces, they are sloughed off. In other instances all of the components of dead and dying cells are degraded and removed by various mechanisms.

Although degradative processes are of great significance in many biologic processes, we are unable to describe mechanisms in any detail. For the present, we can only define the problems and indulge in some speculation. The remarkable progress in understanding protein synthesis has not been balanced by an understanding of what happens at the other end, where the proteins are lost. This ignorance leads to some perplexing questions about systems where we know proteins or organelles are being rapidly lost. For example, when a nerve to rat muscle is cut, the muscle loses about fifty percent of its total substance in 12 days. Although structural proteins such as myosin are lost at a rapid rate, no enzymes capable of degrading myosin have been found in muscle. It would appear that either isolated myosin has been altered so that it is not susceptible to degradation, that very special conditions are required for digestion, or that the macromolecule is lost intact without digestion to small molecules.

A very large number of hydrolytic enzymes have been identified in various organs and cells. These include the cathepsins, which are the intracellular counterparts of pepsin, trypsin, and chymotrypsin. Many peptidases with different specificities, as well as glycosidases, esterases, and nucleases, have also been identified and characterized. These hydrolytic enzymes are usually studied by extracting them from tissues and reacting them with synthetic substrates, or in the case of proteolytic enzymes, with well-characterized substrates such as denatured hemoglobin or casein. It is often assumed that these enzymes are responsible for the degradation of intracellular components, although such components have rarely been tested as substrates.

A great deal of interest in recent years has been directed toward lysosomes, the intracellular organelles, which contain these hydrolytic enzymes in high concentrations. Lysosomes are bounded by a single membrane and are about the size of mitochondria (Fig. 4.11). They can be localized histochemically, usually by testing for acid phosphatase, and can be obtained in quite pure form by density gradient centrifugation. A large number of studies have been carried out on factors

Fig. 4.11 Rat kidney lysosomes (arrows) demonstrated by acid phosphatase stain. Reduced slightly from ×7,600. V — apical vacuoles, M — mitrochondria, N — nucleus, B — basement membrane, BB — brush border. (From Novikoff. 1963. In Lysosomes. Ciba Found. Sympos., J. & A. Churchill, London.)

that stabilize these organelles and on factors that cause activation of their enzymes and rupture of membranes with passage of active enzymes into the cytoplasm. It has been found, for example, that steroid hormone treatment of animals stabilizes lysosomes, while enzymes are released when lysosomes are exposed to such factors as vitamin A, osmotic shock, detergents, freezing and thawing, and mechanical stresses. Morphologic studies have given rise to the concept that lysosomes bring about intracellular digestion, in many cases by combining with organelles that contain the materials to be digested. Figure 4.12 diagrams organelles involved and the sequence of events that is believed to occur in intracellular digestion when lysosomes are intact.

Lysosomes are present in high concentration in liver, kidney, and spleen, but are low in muscle. Although more systematic analyses of organs are required, it appears that the concentration may be proportional to rates of protein or organelle turnover.

Lysosomes have been implicated in several pathologic processes, where they may participate in inflammatory reactions, and in the events leading to antibody synthesis. Circumstantial evidence and a

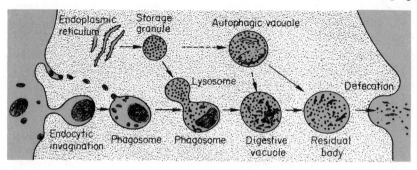

Fig. 4.12 Proposed sequence in intracellular digestion. Storage granules, digestive vacuoles, residual bodies, and autophagic vacuoles are viewed as forms of lysosomes. (From deDuve. 1963. Scientific American. May. Copyright © by Scientific American, Inc. All rights reserved.)

priori considerations also suggest a role for lysosomes and hydrolytic enzymes in aging processes, although contradictory findings indicate that the relationship between these enzymes and organelles and loss of macromolecules is not very straightforward.

In almost all cases where it is known that intracellular degradation is increased, there are increased concentrations of lysosomes and hydrolytic enzymes. These increases are noted in such instances as skeletal muscle wasting, loss of uterine muscle mass following birth, resorption of tadpole tails, and in degenerating and dying cells. Lysosomal enzymes are also increased, however, in regenerating tissue, specifically in regenerating liver following partial hepatectomy, and in regenerating amphibian tails. It has been suggested on the basis of such data that hydrolytic enzymes may play a role in the synthesis of macromolecules. A simple view of intracellular degradation is also made untenable by observations that lysosomal cathepsins appear to be inactivated during kidney necrosis, and that lysosomal enzyme activity is increased only very late in liver cell degeneration. These data have indicated to some workers that lysosomes play a late and somewhat trivial role in scavenging cell debris rather than bringing about generalized loss of cellular constituents.

Very few studies have been carried out on cell components that might serve as substrates for intracellular hydrolytic enzymes. In one study liver lysosomes were isolated, and enzymes were freed by freezing and thawing. Enzymes were then incubated with various fractions of liver cells. The lysosomal preparations actively degraded the liver homogenate, mitochondria, and microsomes, but not nuclei. It has also been observed, however, that muscle lysosomal cathepsins have no detectable activity against actin or myosin, the major structural proteins of muscle.

It would be difficult to avoid the conclusion that cellular enzymes must be responsible for the degradation of most of the components that are known to disappear from cells, although conceivably some components might be lost intact through cell membranes and be degraded at distant sites or excreted. It is clear, however, that intracellular degradation does not consist of simple enzyme-substrate interactions. Very likely, multiple enzymes must act on a single substrate or organelle to cause extensive degradation, substrates must be altered in some way to be recognized by the enzymes, and unusual environmental conditions must be required for activation of the degradative enzymes. We would also assume the existence of feedback mechanisms regulating the synthesis and activation of hydrolytic enzymes, since concentrations of these enzymes and rates of intracellular degradation are highly labile.

Accumulations—functional

If synthesis of an intracellular substance proceeds and there is no effective mechanism of removal or degradation, the substance will accumulate. This accumulation will constitute an aging process. Some accumulations may be functional in the sense that they are useful to tissue or organism, although they may be harmful to the individual cell involved. In these cases, there has presumably been selection favoring evolution of intracellular accumulations. These cases perhaps demonstrate how evolution may result in cellular debility and death for the benefit of the intact organism.

Keratin, a structural protein produced by cells of stratified squamous epithelium, forms a horny impervious layer that protects the epithelium and underlying structures. Steps in the formation and maturation of keratin are analogous to those of collagen. It is first synthesized as a soluble prekeratin, which forms filaments. In mature keratin the filaments are organized into fibrils that are insoluble and resistent to proteolytic enzymes. Chemical inertness is due to a dense cross linking by disulfide bonds. Epithelial cells continue to synthesize keratin until the cell is completely filled, after which no other cellular functions occur. At that stage the cell is essentially a scale of keratin, and is sloughed from the surface. A similar accumulation occurs in cells of the eye lens. In these cells a series of proteins with unusual optical properties, the crystallins and albuminoid, accumulate. Cells containing these proteins lose their nuclei and are converted to fibers, which persist as major components of the lens. Over long periods of time the accumulated lens proteins undergo an additional form of molecular aging, which will be touched on in a later section.

Additional examples of functional accumulation are the cells of holocrine glands. These cells continue to synthesize specialized products until they become filled. They then rupture and release the products. In a sebaceous gland, cells move from the deeper layers, where cell division occurs, toward the gland surface, synthesizing increasing amounts of sebum. By the time they have reached the surface, they consist of bags of sebum.

Other cells have mechanisms for getting rid of cell products, but discrepancies between rate of synthesis and rate of removal may be so out of balance that over the cell's life span a very conspicuous accumulation of products occurs. An example of this is the mucin-producing cell, or goblet cell of the gastrointestinal tract. There is some evidence that accumulation of mucin is cyclical, in which case the criterion of irreversibility required for an aging process would not be satisfied.

Accumulation of pigment

Investigators of histology, using the light microscope, very early observed aggregations of golden brown granules in long-lived cells such as skeletal and cardiac muscle cells and neurones. These granules were usually in a perinuclear position. In cardiac muscle the aggregates characteristically extend from both ends of nuclei (Fig. 4.13). It was apparent that these accumulations increased with age and that similar pigmented granules could be observed in cases of long-standing tissue hypoxia and vitamin E deficiency. The granules have been given a variety of names, such as wear-and-tear, aging, ceroid, and lipofuscin pigments. Lipofuscin appears to be the current designation of choice.

Lipofuscin granules have been studied most extensively in muscle and neurones but have been identified in many organs, notably adrenal cortex, ovarian cells, and interstitial cells of the testis. There is considerable variation between individual cells in concentration, but it is clear that with age both the concentration per cell and the number of cells containing lipofuscin increase. In the dog the percentage of myocardium taken up by lipofuscin pigment increases steadily with age (Fig. 4.14). Similar measurements have been made of human myocardial lipofuscin, and it is of interest that the rate of accumulation in the dog is about 5.5 times as fast as in the human, whereas human beings have a life span about 5.5 times that of the dog. That is, old dogs and old humans have approximately the same amount of lipofuscin. This indicates that pigment formation is not the consequence of simple reactions that are only time and temperature dependent,

Fig. 4.13   Lipofuscin granules in cardiac muscle. Reduced slightly from ×600. (From Strehler. 1964. Adv. in Gerontol. Res. 1:343.)

Fig. 4.14   Percentage of myocardial volume occupied by lipofuscin pigment as a function of age in dogs. (From Munnell and Getty. 1968. J. Gerontol. 23:154.)

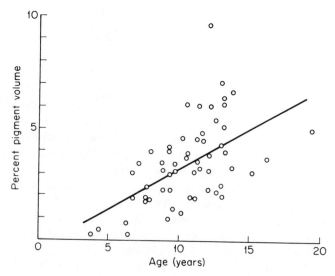

but that accumulation results from metabolic reactions that occur at different rates in mammals with different life spans.

Ultrastructure of the granules is quite variable. They may occur as dense aggregates of very small granules or as organelles containing vacuoles of varying size (Fig. 4.15). Peripheral membranes are present

Fig. 4.15 Vacuolated pigment granules in adrenal cell of 20-month-old mouse. Reduced slightly from ×18,000. (From Samorajski and Ordy. 1967. J. Gerontol. **22**:253.)

in some cases. They are very heterogeneous structures by chemical analysis. They contain many lipids of known composition. These include lecithin, cephalin, sphingomyelin, and cholesterol esters. Also, many glycerides and saturated and unsaturated hydrocarbons have been identified. It is generally believed that a large component of lipofuscin consists of macromolecules formed by oxidative polymerization reactions of unsaturated lipids. Protein also constitutes a significant fraction of the granules, and a number of enzyme activities have been identified. These include hydrolytic enzymes of the type found in lysosomes, as well as respiratory enzymes. The granules contain acidic groups, and it has been suggested that some of these components may be adsorbed to their surface.

The genesis of lipofuscin granules is not known. It has been postulated by various investigators that they represent degenerated mitochondria or lysosomes, that they are unique organelles which sequester harmful intracellular garbage, or that they are formed by cross linking of elements of the endoplasmic reticulum. Their increase represents a true aging process in which aggregation and polymerization appear to occur, resulting in the accumulation of substances for which there is no adequate mechanism of removal.

Accumulation of minerals

The accumulation of minerals, particularly calcium salts, in connective tissue with age was mentioned in an earlier chapter. Similar accumulations might be expected in cells, in view of the fact that crystal formation and growth represent aging processes which should take place wherever ions are present in significant concentrations for long periods.

Several decades ago a number of observations gave rise to the concept that rapidly dividing cells such as those in neoplasms had very low concentrations of calcium, while cells which were stable or slowly dividing had high concentrations. It was reported that calcium ions increased with age in the cortex of cells from plants, rotifers, planarians, and an amphibian. An age-related increase in cellular binding of calcium was claimed on the basis of experiments in which increased calcium was found in the livers of mature mice, compared to young mice, after the injection of a calcium isotope. Contradictory results were obtained when a variety of organs from rats of different ages were homogenized and incubated with calcium. No difference in calcium binding with age was noted.

Although data on calcium binding are equivocal, it has been suggested that such binding may be harmful to cells on the basis of experiments in which longevity of unfertilized invertebrate eggs and rotifers was achieved by decreasing calcium in the media, and by citrate treatment to remove calcium.

Whereas calcium is predominantly extracellular, magnesium has a higher concentration within cells. One study has indicated that the latter ion increases in concentration with age in human smooth and skeletal muscle.

On the basis of current information, one cannot generalize about mineralization of cells with age. Additional systematic studies, employing more modern methods of tissue fractionation and elemental analyses, are required.

Aging of stable and structural cell components

Many cells contain structural macromolecules that have very low rates of turnover. Contractile proteins of muscle, which comprise a large fraction of the total body protein, are examples. Other structural components of cells such as membranes would be expected to have low rates of turnover because of their insolubility and complex organization, although very little is really known about their metabolism. Any macromolecules present at a given site for long periods would be good candidates for aging. The possible histone binding to DNA and gross morphological changes in chromosomes with age have been mentioned earlier.

Among intracellular macromolecules that would be expected to age are the eye lens proteins. These proteins consist of several populations of soluble molecules, the crystallins; and an insoluble protein or group of proteins known as albuminoid. With age, the amount of insoluble albuminoid increases. In the rat, as shown in Fig. 4.16, the insoluble protein increases up to about two years of age and then remains constant. Soluble protein does not increase at as fast a rate, and decreases from around 50 to 90 weeks. Albuminoid, as percentage of total pro-

Fig. 4.16 Amounts of soluble and insoluble eye lens protein in the rat as a function of age. (Redrawn from Dische, et al. 1956. Arch. Ophthalmol. **55**:471.)

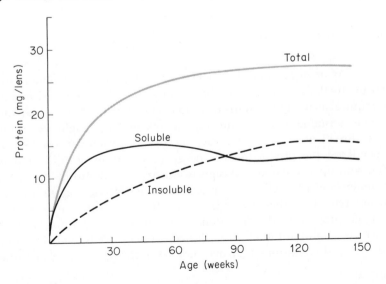

tein, increases up to about two years of age. This increase is associated with a decreasing concentration of one of the crystallins, γ crystallin, as well as with a decrease in water content of the lens. These data are consistent with the view that newly synthesized proteins are soluble and that, with age, one or more of the soluble proteins aggregate to form the insoluble albuminoid. Both disulphide and hydrogen bonds have been implicated in the formation of insoluble aggregates. Such an intracellular aggregation bears a close resemblance to the progressive cross linking and insolubilization of the extracellular protein, collagen. It is not known whether insoluble lens protein undergoes a progressive cross linking with age similar to collagen.

Very conspicuous age-changes in collagen were detected by measuring osmotic swelling ability, which is a manifestation of the modulus of elasticity, as discussed in the last chapter. Similar studies have been made of human myocardium to determine if an age-related aggregation or cross linking of intracellular muscle proteins occurred. After the cessation of growth, there is a marked decrease in the ability of heart muscle to swell (Fig. 4.17). This indicates the appearance with age of a factor that prevents the structural proteins from separating from one another. Subsequent studies showed that the age difference did not persist at the subcellular level and might, therefore, be due to the cell membranes or connective tissue, rather than the contractile proteins. Solubility studies of the contractile proteins of skeletal muscle have not revealed any changes suggesting a progressive cross linking with age. Only preliminary studies have been undertaken of structural proteins of muscle, and cell membranes have been neglected entirely in regard to age.

Degeneration in vitro

As mentioned earlier, isolated populations of macromolecules and organelles are either unstable so that they deteriorate with time, or require such rigidly controlled environmental conditions that they become unstable as environmental factors undergo slight variations. It is also likely that the stability of these intracellular constituents depends on the production of energy in the form of ATP and on their continual function. Concepts of this type are useful in attempting to understand why cellular components, either isolated or within cells, do not remain as they are indefinitely. In other words, why do they undergo progressive deteriorations that satisfy the definition of aging processes? Maintaining intracellular constituents, cells, and tissues under artificial conditions that may not be optimal, and in which they

Fig. 4.17 Swelling ability of human myocardium as a function of age. (From Kohn and Rollerson. 1959. Proc. Soc. Exptl. Biol. Med. **100:253**.)

do not function normally, gives some indications of the types of deterioration that occur more or less spontaneously.

Maintaining rat leukocytes under what would appear to be close to ideal conditions results in a rapid loss of enzyme activity, as shown in Fig. 4.8. Cell membranes also become altered in that normal membranes exclude the dye Trypan blue, while there is a progressive decrease in the number of cells that can exclude this dye on incubation in vitro. There is also a loss of protein during incubation.

When the intrastructure of these incubated cells is examined by electron microscopy, progressive alterations in all components are observed. As shown in Fig. 4.18, the cell and nuclear membranes become very indistinct between 4 and 8 hours. Nuclear material appears to undergo a rearrangement and then to become more uniformly granular and indistinct after 3 hours. Cytoplasmic granules decrease in number and become poorly defined after 3 hours. These changes

Fig. 4.18 Changes with time in rat neutrophils maintained in vitro. Culture age in hours is indicated for each picture.

can be best characterized as a generalized structural deterioration that is not caused by any external injury or insult. Similar widespread degenerations have been described in liver cells in vitro. Mechanisms of these degenerations at the molecular level are unknown, but may consist of activation or release of hydrolytic enzymes with cleavage of bonds in structural macromolecules, local changes in pH that solubilize certain components, or a redistribution of inorganic ions that alters the colloidal state of molecular aggregations.

An overview

Both experimental evidence and a priori considerations seem to indicate that macromolecules, organelles, and structural elements such as membranes and chromosomes deteriorate or undergo morphological aberrations with time. Although it has not been feasible to observe a given intracellular component change in situ under normal conditions, it is possible that components which turn over undergo these alterations, and probable that the degenerative changes occur in short-lived cells which degenerate themselves. There is no convincing evidence that renewable components become altered in long-lived cells; that is, that newly synthesized components in old cells are different from similar components of young cells.

It has also not been shown that long-lived cells lose their capacity to synthesize components, although chromosomal aberrations and possible histone-DNA aggregations have been observed with time. Some changes in enzyme content and in properties of organelles in cells and organs of different ages have been reported, but it is not known if these represent irreversible, intrinsic aging processes, or if they are the consequences of altered function at higher levels of organization.

It is clear that insoluble pigmented macromolecular aggregates accumulate in long-lived cells, and that several types of insoluble substances accumulate in specialized cells. It also appears likely that minerals accumulate in certain types of cells.

Finally, many of the most interesting questions we might ask have received little or no attention. A large number of possible intracellular age-changes has been neither excluded nor proven.

Some research for the future

1. Turnover and stability. Many structures such as cell and nuclear membranes, fibrils, and tubules may be present for long periods and undergo changes with age. More data are required on the turnover of these structures. Studies utilizing new fractionation techniques in combination with isotope labeling should be informative.

2. Aging of structural components. The above structures might be isolated and studied as a function of age in regard to chemical composition, particularly mineral binding, and in regard to enzyme content, cross linking of subunits, and permeability.

3. Aging in normal turnover. By inhibiting synthesis in cells it might be possible to follow populations of macromolecules and organelles through the degradative phase of the turnover cycle. Studies of their properties should indicate whether they undergo age-changes prior to degradation.

4. Synthetic capacity in short-lived cells. Populations of rapidly turning-over cells with short life spans could be studied in situ by histochemical techniques, or, after the last cell division, by chemical methods to determine whether the ability to synthesize metabolic enzymes is lost as specialized cell products are formed.

5. Degradative processes. Intracellular components that are known to be lost or degraded could be isolated and incubated with various cell fractions in an attempt to identify enzyme systems responsible for degradation. Factors that activate or stimulate synthesis of these systems could then be studied.

REFERENCES

Austin, C. R. 1967. Chromosome deterioration in ageing eggs of the rabbit. Nature. **213**:1018.

Barrows, C. H. and L. M. Roeder. 1961. Effect of age on protein synthesis in rats. J. Gerontol. **16**:321.

Detwiler, T. C. and H. H. Draper. 1962. Physiological aspects of aging. IV. Senescent changes in the metabolism and composition of nucleic acids of the liver and muscle in the rat. J. Gerontol. **17**:138.

Gold, P. H., M. V. Gee, and B. L. Strehler. 1968. Effect of age on oxidative phosphorylation in the rat. J. Gerontol. **23**:509.

Gutmann, E., B. Jakoubek, I. Hájek, V. Rohlícek, and J. Škaloud. 1962. Effect of age on proteosynthesis in spinal motoneurones following nerve interruption as shown by histoautoradiography of S[35] labelled methionine. Physiol. Bohemoslov. **11**:437.

Mukundan, M. A., A. Devi, and N. K. Sarkar. 1963. Effect of age on the incorporation of C[14] thymidine into DNA, catalysed by soluble extract of rat liver. Biochem. Biophys. Res. Commun. **11**:353.

Sayeed, M. M. and H. T. Blumenthal. 1968. Age difference in the intestinal phosphomonoesterase activity of mice. Proc. Soc. Exptl. Biol. Med. **129**:1.

Thorup, O. A., J. T. Carpenter, and P. Howard. 1964. Human erythrocyte catalase: demonstration of heterogeneity and relationship to erythrocyte ageing in vivo. Brit. J. Haematol. **10**:542.

Van Gastel, C. and C. Bishop. 1968. Changes in activities of some enzymes during in vivo aging of mouse erythrocytes. Proc. Soc. Exptl. Biol. Med. **127**:1067.

Zorzoli, A. 1968. Fumarase activity in mouse tissues during development and aging. J. Gerontol. **23**:506.

FIVE

Aging of Cells

At the level of complexity of the cell we become concerned for the first time with aging of a living system. Changes of interest will be those which are progressive and which are manifested by alterations in function of the system. At the level of the cell the end points of death or degeneration are more discernible than they are in the case of subcellular substances or structures. It will also be clear that aging of the cell as a system may proceed independently of the aging of some of its components. In other words, the cell may be in a steady state while populations of macromolecules and organelles are degenerating and being replaced. Or the cell may degenerate and die while many of its components are not significantly altered.

As systems become more complex, the number of ways in which aging problems can be approached increases. Questions arise concerning the probability of reaching end points as a function of time. Frequently the most obvious changes with age are in functional or gross morphological characteristics. These are secondary to more basic changes at the molecular level—that is, they are manifestations of fundamental aging processes. It is important conceptually to distinguish aging processes that can be observed from primary molecular changes that might be responsible. We can often describe in general terms the manifestations of cell aging, and we may know about some basic subcellular changes or be able to suggest some reasonable hypotheses. However, it will be apparent that no cause and effect sequences relating basic changes to debilities of age have been proved.

Rates at which cells age and ways in which aging is manifested vary from one type of cell population to another. Before we discuss cell aging, a classification of types of cell populations is required.

78

The different kinds of cell populations

There are many ways of classifying cell populations. The classification scheme most useful in regard to aging is based on cell life span and on the capacity of cells to divide, or on frequency of cell division. No classification is entirely satisfactory. However, most cell types can be fitted into categories described by Cowdry. These categories, with some modifications, are as follows:

Vegetative intermitotic cells

These are cells that are continuously or periodically dividing. They are the unspecialized primordial or stem cells that give rise to populations of specialized cells. Examples of these stem cells are the basal cells of epidermis, hemocytoblasts of bone marrow, spermatogonia, and primitive crypt cells of intestine. Each cell as an entity exists only between mitoses.

Differentiating intermitotic cells

These cells arise from vegetative intermitotics. They are more highly developed than the stem cells; evidence of specialization is usually apparent. They also divide more or less on schedule, although duration of existence between mitoses varies widely in different populations. Erythroblasts and myeloblasts of the red and white blood cell lines, respectively, and spermatocytes exist between mitoses for very short periods. Other partially differentiated cells, such as those in liver, divide infrequently.

Reverting post mitotic cells

These are mature, highly specialized cells which do not normally divide, or which divide rarely unless they receive stimulation. They retain the capacity to divide, however, and some of them may proliferate very rapidly under certain circumstances. Examples of cells in this category are fibrocytes, chondrocytes, osteocytes, endothelial cells, and kidney cells. Some liver cells that divide at a fast rate in regeneration might be placed in this group.

Short-lived fixed post mitotic cells

These are the mature cells that arise from the differentiating intermitotics. They are the final products of cell populations that are turning over in what appears to be a programmed fashion. As they degenerate, they are replaced by cells from the differentiating inter-mitotic series. The fixed post mitotics do not divide. Granulocytic leukocytes, red blood cells, keratinizing squamous cells, mucus, acid, and enzyme-producing cells of the gastrointestinal tract are examples.

Long-lived fixed post mitotic cells

These cells also do not divide. However, rather than being members of turning-over populations, they are formed early in the life of the animal and persist rather indefinitely. The best examples are neurones. Muscle cells, although they have a limited capacity to divide, do not normally do so, and are therefore included in this group.

Differences in life span between different mammalian cells are enormous. Certain white blood cells in the human being have life spans measured in hours, whereas neurones and muscle cells are capable of living at least as long as the oldest person. Since these different types of cells presumably started off with the same genetic potential, differences in life span represent a remarkable divergence in controls of gene expression.

Aging of intermitotics

One would not expect cells that exist between mitoses to un-dergo any changes that could be considered aging. At each mitosis two new cells are born. Theoretically, however, progressive alterations could occur in certain components which could be carried on into the next generation. The significance of such changes would then depend on the rate of alteration as compared to the rates of new syntheses and cell division. Some years ago it was claimed that cumulative cellular changes, occurring over many generations, had been demon-strated in rotifers. These findings have not been repeated, however, nor shown to occur in other species. On the other hand, it has been clearly shown that changes occur in proliferating cells in tissue culture. These studies will be discussed below.

It has not been feasible to study the properties of a given cell be-tween mitoses in an animal. If changes occur in intermitotics they should be inferred from or detected in altered populations of cells studied at different times over the life span of an animal. Such alter-ations might be in chemical composition, in metabolic activity, in numbers of cells, or in ability to divide. As in the case of intracellular components, discussed in the previous chapter, number of cells and their activity are frequently the results of extrinsic feedback mechanisms. For that reason we must be conservative in judging an age-related observation; what would appear to be a progressive cellular change might be reversible. It could be due to an extrinsic cause, and be more a measure of the physiological state of the animal than of aging cells. Thus, the capacity of cells to divide would be more significant than the number present.

Changes with age in reverting fixed post mitotics have not been systematically studied. However, proliferation of fibroblasts, capillary, bone, and cartilage cells in response to tissue injury has been observed frequently in animals and human beings of different ages. No significant differences related to age in the ability of these cells to divide or function have been noted. *wrong*

Rate of cell division as a function of age has been studied in several vegetative intermitotic populations. Crypt cells of the mouse small intestine are stem cells that divide and give rise to more highly specialized cells. If radioactive component of DNA is injected, it will be rapidly incorporated into cells that are synthesizing DNA. The tissue can then be sampled at various times, and the percentage of cells in mitosis that contain the label can be determined by autoradiography. The time between one cell division and the next (generation time) can be measured, because when the cells that are synthesizing DNA at the time of administration of the label divide, 100% of the cells in mitosis will be labeled. Time between highest or lowest percentage values will be the generation time. Duration of the 100% peak may also be used as a measure of the time during which DNA was being synthesized when the labeled precursor was present.

From the data in Fig. 5.1, it can be seen that there is a definite lengthening of generation time during the animal's growth period, and a probable slight lengthening between maturity and old age. It was calculated that the generation time rose from 10.1 hours at 55 days of age to 14.1 hours at 300 days. It then remained quite constant until 675 days, rising subsequently to 15.7 hours at 1050 days of age. Increases in generation time were in the time during which DNA was synthesized and in the period in the cell cycle immediately before DNA synthesis. There is also some evidence that the population of proliferating crypt cells declines with age. On the basis of numbers of cells labeled, it was calculated that there were 126 proliferating cells per crypt in 100-day-old mice, and 89 in 825-day-old animals.

The number of intestinal epithelial cells does not change with age. Since the proliferating crypt cells give rise to short-lived fixed post mitotics, and show both a decrease in number and a lengthened generation time with age, life spans of the fixed post mitotics must be increased with increasing age of the animals.

Fig. 5.1 Generation cycle of intestinal epithelium of mice. Age of mice in days indicated for each curve. (Redrawn from Lesher. 1966. Radiation and Ageing. Taylor and Francis, Ltd., London.)

In terms of intermitotic cell aging, it will be apparent that changes in number of dividing crypt cells and generation times do not occur linearly as a function of animal age. In the very old animals that are about to die, a large proportion of the crypt cells are seen to be dividing with only a slight prolongation of generation time, compared to the cells of young adult animals. We cannot decide from these data if an individual intermitotic cell in an older animal is different from one in a younger animal. Such factors as alterations in feeding habits and activity and in blood supply to the gut, which might influence the rate at which the isotope is supplied to crypt cells, might influence the experimental results. Since these factors would tend to maximize age differences, the data are consistent with the view that these intermitotics do not change very significantly with age.

The liver has been a useful organ to study in regard to cell proliferation as a function of age. Cells rarely divide in an adult liver; about one out of 10,000 to 20,000 cells is in mitosis at any time. However, if lobes of the liver are removed, approximately 70 percent of the liver in most experiments, cells in remaining lobes proliferate rapidly and reconstitute most of the original liver mass in a few days. This is an excellent example of the lability of cell division rates, and suggests the extent to which rates might be influenced by control or feedback mechanisms.

Bucher and co-workers have investigated liver regeneration in rats of different ages. They used young growing rats 4 to 6 weeks old, 4 to 8-month-old adult rats, and 21 to 30-month-old rats. The very young animals regenerated liver more rapidly than the older animals. There was no difference, however, in rate of regeneration between adult and old rats (Fig. 5.2). The actual rate of DNA synthesis early in

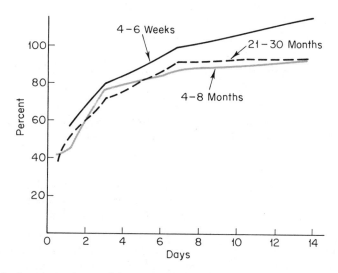

Fig. 5.2 Percentage of original liver mass restored following partial hepatectomy in rats, corrected for changes in body weight. Ages of animals indicated for each curve. (Redrawn from Bucher and Glinos. 1950. Canc. Res. **10:**324.)

regeneration was investigated by injecting a radioactive DNA precursor at various times after removal of liver, and measuring specific activity of DNA after two hours. As shown in Fig. 5.3, liver of weanling rats gave two peaks of maximum DNA labeling. This indicates that cell division of two cell populations is synchronized. In 4-month-old animals only one population of DNA-synthesizing cells is identified, and the curve is spread out, indicating less synchrony. Still less synchrony is apparent in the case of 12 to 15-month-old rats. The onset of DNA synthesis in the young adults lags about three hours after that in the weanling rats, while synthesis in the older animals lags by 8 to 12 hours. By 50 hours, which is still early in regeneration, there is no difference in rate of DNA synthesis between 4- and 12 to 15-month-old animals.

The authors point out that the shapes and time relationships of

Fig. 5.3 Rates of DNA synthesis in livers from rats of different ages following partial hepatectomy. (Redrawn from Bucher, et al. 1964. Canc. Res. 24:509.)

these curves are valid for comparisons, but that heights of the curves are of questionable value because they depend on specific activity of the isotope at the site of DNA synthesis, which could be altered by a number of uncontrolled or unknown variables. In addition, the normal rate of liver cell division varies with growth rate. If rates of DNA synthesis in regenerating liver are compared to rates in normal liver, it is found that there is a 20-fold increase in weanlings, a 50-fold increase in young adults, and a 125-fold increase in the older animals. It could thus be argued that there is an increased proliferative capacity with age. This might not be so, however, since the DNA precursor pool is larger in younger animals, and this might dilute the isotope, causing newly synthesized DNA to have a lower specific activity.

These arguments serve to demonstrate the difficulties in inferring a basic mechanism from a general observation. As in the case of gut epithelium, it appears that the greatest changes in the proliferative pattern of liver cells are associated with changes in the growth rate of the animal. It is of particular interest that a population of cells that synthesizes DNA in weanling animals may not be able to do so in adults. In terms of aging after slowing of growth in the animals, initial proliferative response to a stimulus is delayed. This delay could be due either to intrinsic cellular aging changes or to environmental causes. Regardless of animal age, however, liver cells are capable of dividing and reconstituting liver tissue that is apparently normal in mass and function. This would suggest that there are no fundamental differences in liver intermitotics as the animal ages.

In a stratified squamous epithelium, individual stem cells and mitoses can be identified histologically, and cells synthesizing DNA can be localized by autoradiography. The effect of animal age on numbers of stem or progenitor cells and on DNA synthesis as a measure of frequency of division has been studied at two sites in the rat. As shown in Fig. 5.4, in the period from 2 to 9 months of age while

	2 mo.	9 mo.	19 mo.	27 mo.
Palate				
No. of progenitor cells				
per mm	231.2	230.6	185.8	149.0
Synthesis index	20.5	11.4	14.1	16.5
Tongue				
No. of progenitor cells				
per mm	255.3	269.9	253.3	185.2
Synthesis index	16.8	12.3	13.5	19.0

Fig. 5.4 Progenitor population and synthesis index of two epithelial cell populations in rats of different ages. (From Sharav and Massler. 1967. Exptl. Cell. Res. 47:132.)

animals are maturing, the number of stem cells remains rather constant, while the percentage of cells synthesizing DNA prior to division at a given time (synthesis index) decreases. After 9 months, as animals age, there is a decrease in the number of progenitor cells and an increase in the synthesis index. As a result of these two changes, the actual number of dividing cells does not change with age, and the tissue turnover rate also remains relatively constant.

Red blood cells arise from intermitotic cells in the bone marrow. They age in the circulation and, as the old cells disappear, they are replaced by young cells arising from division of the bone marrow cells. There is a continuous turnover by which the level of circulating red cells is kept constant. Turnover of these cells in 6- and 18-month-old rats was studied by labeling circulating red cells with radioactive chromium, and injecting cells from young animals into young and old rats, and cells from old animals into young and old rats. It was found that rates of disappearance of labeled cells with time was the same in all four groups. This indicated that rates of red cell formation and destruction were independent of age.

The problem of stem cell division in bone marrow as a function of animal age has been approached in an unusual way. If bone marrow cells are injected into an animal that has been irradiated, individual cells will lodge in the spleen and divide, giving rise to nodules of cells that can easily be observed and counted. When a standard number of bone marrow cells from mice of various ages was injected into standard recipients, it was found that the number of splenic colonies increased with increasing age of donors up to 18 months of age, followed by a rather abrupt decrease by 20 months, and a slightly smaller decline by 24 months. This was interpreted as indicating that the number of stem cells capable of dividing increased to the age of 18 months and then declined. This concept fitted very well with other data showing that maximum resistence to death by radiation damage to marrow was at around 18 months of age.

Rate of stem cell division in the marrow is very susceptible to control by a number of factors. Production of red cells is stimulated by any change causing a diminished oxygen supply to tissues, as well as by cobalt in the diet. When weanling, young adult, and old rats were given excessive amounts of cobalt, and a second series was placed daily in a low-pressure chamber for 45 days, all the animals showed a marked increase in hematocrit (number of circulating red cells, as percentage by volume of blood), and no age-related differences between old and adult rats in extent or rate of increase were apparent. When the three groups of animals were exposed to low pressure for 94 days, by 40 to 50 days hematocrits of the weanling, young, and old rats were 67, 71, and 63 percent, respectively (Fig. 5.5). Thus, with a marked stress, there appeared a rather modest decline in proliferative response with age.

An experiment with marrow proliferative capacity, analagous to the liver regeneration experiments, was performed. The three groups of rats were bled to remove blood equal to 2 percent of the body weight. Times required for return of hematocrit to normal levels, and numbers of circulating reticulocytes (nucleated red cells from recent cell divisions) as functions of time after bleeding were determined. As shown in Fig. 5.6, the only age difference is a slight sluggishness in response in the oldest animals.

The authors conclude from these studies that changes in the marrow intermitotics with age, if any, are subtle.

Lymphocytes have received a great deal of attention because of their role in the immune response. Circulating lymphocytes do not normally divide, but they can be made to do so by treatment with phytohemaglutinin. When lymphocytes from human beings from one to 98 years of age were stimulated to divide, there was enormous in-

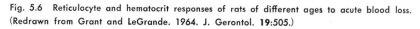

Fig. 5.5 Hematocrits of rats of different ages when exposed to ambient pressure of 380 mm Hg. (Redrawn from Grant and LeGrande. 1964. J. Gerontol. **19:**505.)

Fig. 5.6 Reticulocyte and hematocrit responses of rats of different ages to acute blood loss. (Redrawn from Grant and LeGrande. 1964. J. Gerontol. **19:**505.)

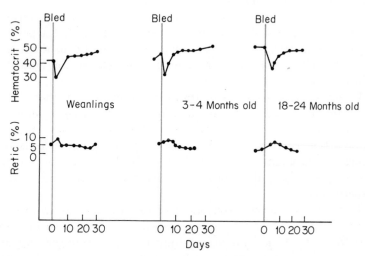

dividual variation in response at all ages, and little or no change with age was apparent.

An important question about intermitotics is whether or not they age in any way that is related to the age of the animals that contain them. One way to study this is to transplant a population of inter-mitotic cells from animal to animal, and then to determine if this population of turning-over cells lives as long as or longer than the host or donor. Studies of this type have been carried out by Krohn, using mouse skin. Skin contains stratified squamous epithelium, hair follicles, and sebaceous glands, all of which consist of turning-over cell populations.

Krohn's procedure is to transplant a piece of skin onto a mouse, and after time has passed to transfer the same graft to another mouse, and so on. As a graft heals into place, there is a scarring around the periphery which diminishes the size of the graft. As the same bit of skin is passed through several graftings, it gets smaller and smaller, until it can no longer be transferred. It was found that skin persisted through transplantations for 4½ to 5 years before it became too small. This is about twice as long as a mouse's mean life span. The maximum recorded life span of a mouse at the time of these studies was 3½ years.

Differences in viability when old and young skin were transplanted to young mice were equivocal. Krohn transplanted parental skin to hybrids so that grafts could be identified by difference in hair color. With one strain combination, skin from old donors did not persist as long as skin from young donors, and appeared to age in situ. With another strain combination, however, no differences with regard to age of donor were apparent.

These studies do not tell us whether or not these intermitotics are intrinsically immortal. They do indicate, however, that a population of stem cells is capable of dividing and giving rise to differentiated tissue for a much longer time than the life span of the animal from which it is obtained.

It should be noted that in transplantation of skin, the connective tissue dermis is also transplanted. This is primarily collagenous tissue, which has little or no turnover. Thus, the graft consists, in part, of aging tissue from the original donor. Environmental effects of this aging matrix might eventually limit the viability of cells and be the cause of transplant deterioration, which was seen in some of Krohn's experiments.

In reviewing the data on aging of intermitotics in an attempt to answer one of the original questions—whether or not an intermitotic cell from an old animal differs from one in a younger animal—we must conclude that there is no evidence that this is so. In terms of cell division, it appears that in some systems the rates are correlated with rates of growth of the animal. Probably changes of this type that are part of growth should not be considered aging processes. As animals age, one gains the impression that intermitotics continue to maintain tissues in a steady state and are capable of proliferating in response to stimuli to reestablish the normal level of functioning cells. It also appears likely that numbers of stem cells are in great excess in younger animals, and that there is probably some loss with age. When subjected to stress, some systems in older animals appear somewhat sluggish in their response, even though they finally achieve the required results. Such delayed responses could be due to many extracellular factors.

It is clear that there is no generalized loss of stem cells that is directly related to life span of animals. There is also no time course for loss of stem cells that is characteristic of all populations. As suggested by the above observations, some populations show no decline, others may decrease slightly very late in life, and others might show a slight decline following maturity.

Death of stem cells could be caused by intracellular accidents, by mutations, or by extrinsic factors such as inadequate nutrition or the accumulation of toxic materials in the environment. Losses have not been sufficiently documented for us to know that they represent aging processes, in that cells die in greater numbers with increasing time. Some studies of cells in tissue culture suggest changes that might occur in rapidly dividing cells.

Aging of cells in tissue culture

Cells that are propagated in culture can be viewed as intermitotics that have been freed from their natural tissue environment. They are useful in the study of aging in several ways: effects of environmental factors, which might vary with age, on proliferating cells can be determined, properties of dividing cell populations from animals of different ages can be observed, and intrinsic cellular age-changes may become apparent.

Tissue culture media are frequently enriched with serum or embryo extract. It was discovered early that plasma or serum from old animals inhibited cell proliferation. As shown in Fig. 5.7, with increasing age of the animals from which plasma is obtained, there is a progressive decline in rate of cell proliferation and in life span of populations. It was subsequently found that both a protein and lipid fraction from old serum was inhibitory. This suggests that in old animals, some stem cells might be poisoned by toxic factors in blood. As animals age, their homeostatic mechanisms become less efficient, a factor which will be dealt with in some detail later. It is not unlikely that a variety of

Donor age	Av. no. of passages before growth cessation	Av. relative rate of outgrowth
6 weeks	20	148
3 months	13	100
3 years	8	51
9 years	2	22

After Carrel and Ebeling (1921).

Fig. 5.7 Effect of plasma from chickens of various ages on fibroblast outgrowth. (From Hay. 1967. Adv. in Gerontol. Res. 2:121.)

inhibitory substances that are excreted or metabolized in young animals accumulate in the blood of older animals.

When small bits of tissue are placed in culture, there is a lag period before proliferating cells migrate out from the main mass. This lag period becomes longer, the older the animal from which the explant is obtained (Fig. 5.8). In the case of liver explants, the older the donor, the less the percentage of explants that show growth and the longer

Fig. 5.8 Latent period before cellular emigration from various organ explants. (From Hay. 1967. Adv. in Gerontol. Res. 2:121.)

Tissue	Donor age	Latent period	Source
Chicken spleen	14–16-day embryo Adult	<2 hours 12 hours	Carrel and Burrows (1911)
Chicken heart	4-day embryo 8-day embryo 14-day embryo 18-day embryo	4.9 hours 5.5 hours 9.3 hours 11 hours	Cohn and Murray (1925)
Chicken thoracic aorta	Adult	3–5 days	Simms and Stillman (1936–1937)
Chicken heart	5–7-day embryo 20-day embryo 1 year	6 hours 10–12 hours 28–120 hours	Hoffman *et al.* (1937)
Rat liver	4–8 weeks 4–8 months 18–24 months	58 hours 82 hours 96 hours	Glinos and Bartlett (1951)

the lag period. If regenerating liver is used, the age differences are no longer apparent. There is some evidence that the increasing lag period with increasing age of donor is due to extracellular factors. Treatment of explants by hydrolytic enzymes such as papain, elastase, and collagenase shortens the lag period. It has been suggested that cell proliferation and movement are hindered by the connective tissue matrix in which the cells are imbedded. Age-changes in components of connective tissue such as cross linking of proteins and loss of polysaccharide, discussed in Ch. 3, might cause the variations in explant behavior with aging of donors.

Many studies of cells in culture suggested that the populations were immortal—that they would go on dividing forever if kept in an ideal medium and at an optimum cell concentration. It was discovered, however, that some cell lines would proliferate indefinitely while other lines would die out after a certain number of generations or subcultures, no matter how well they were treated. It appeared that the cultures that died out consisted of normal diploid cells. The cell lines that appeared immortal often took on some of the characteristics of cancer cells, in showing aneuploidy or chromosomal abnormalities.

The dying out of normal human diploid cells in culture has been studied in detail by Hayflick. Using fetal lung fibroblasts, he found that the cultures died out after about 50 passages, or 50 generations, taking slightly less than one year. As shown in Fig. 5.9, the number of viable cells remained high for a long period during subcultures, and then dropped off quite abruptly. Loss of cells was exponential during the dying-out phase. The resulting curve represents the dying out of an aging population, in that the probability of dying increases

Fig. 5.9 Cell counts at successive passages (2:1 dilution ratio) of cultures of human fetal lung cells. (Redrawn from Hayflick. 1965. Exptl. Cell Res. 37:614.)

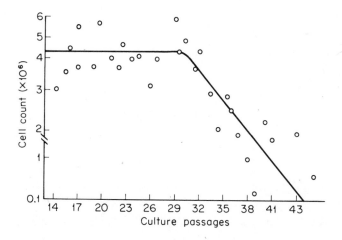

with increasing time. Possibly dying out is more related to the passage of time than to the number of cell divisions, since cultures that were subcultured in different ways varied in numbers of doublings but died out at around the same time.

Hayflick also found that the number of doublings before dying out depended on the age of the human being from whom the cells were obtained. Thus, from embryos, cells were capable of 50 ± 10 doublings; between birth and maturity, 30 ± 10; over 20 years of age, 20 ± 10 doublings. It is perhaps significant that no differences were detected between cells from young and old adults. Figure 5.10 gives comparative data for doublings of cell lines from fetal and old individuals. It is worth noting, for the discussion of animal aging in a later section, that cells from an 87-year-old individual are capable of 29 doublings.

It is not known why these cultured cells die out. Obvious explanations such as latent viruses, alterations in media, and dying out of

Fig. 5.10   Numbers of cell doublings before growth decline of cell strains from human fetuses and adults. (From Hay. 1967. Adv. in Gerontol. Res. 2:121.)

Fetal lung		*Adult lung*			
Strain	*Cell doublings*	*Strain*	*Cell doublings*	*Donor age*	*Cause of death*
WI-1	51	WI-1000	29	87	Heart failure
WI-3	35	WI-1001	18	80	CVA
WI-11	57	WI-1002	21	69	Bronchial pneumonia
WI-16	44	WI-1003	24	67	Dissecting aneurysm
WI-18	53	WI-1004	22	61	Renal failure
WI-19	50	WI-1005	16	58	Rheumatoid arthritis
WI-23	55	WI-1006	14	58	Pulmonary embolus
WI-24	39	WI-1007	20	26	Auto accident
WI-25	41				
WI-26	50				
WI-27	41				
WI-38	48				
WI-44	63				

necessary "feeder cells" in originally mixed cultures appear to have been excluded. Among the remaining possibilities are an accumulation of accidents or mutations in DNA or other non-turning-over macromolecules or the slow accumulation of some harmful substance from the medium. Also, cell growth and division occurring over a long period could result in the diluting out of some cell component that cannot be reproduced at a sufficient rate.

Considerable speculation has been stimulated on the possible role of limited cell generations, as described by Hayflick, in stem cell division and survival in an animal. A great many calculations have been made to determine if any cell lines in an animal go through more than 50 generations. Different conclusions have been reached, primarily because it is not known whether all stem cells divide regularly, to what extent a group of stem cells is homogeneous in terms of past number of generations, or whether one cell may be the result of three past divisions while the adjacent cell may have had 20 divisions in its past. It would certainly appear that 50 generations per fetal cell is greatly in excess over what would be required over an animal's life span. Starting with two cells, 50 generations would give around 1000 liters of cells. Considering the entire fetus, the volume of cells that could be produced is truly astronomical.

Obviously, the rapid and prolonged proliferation of cells that occurs in tissue culture does not occur in vivo. Also, in vivo, no population of stem cells is known to die out in one year in the adult. Nor do stem cells in an animal continue to give rise only to stem cells. Probably close to half of all cells arising from stem cell division differentiate to fixed postmitotic cells.

Although large numbers of stem cells do not die in the animal as they do in tissue culture, some systems show a slight decline in numbers with increasing age, as described earlier. It is possible that the cells that are lost are the ones that have resulted from the most divisions. Limited capacity for cell division might then be listed among the possible causes for loss of intermitotics as a function of age.

Aging of short-lived fixed postmitotics

The distinction between cell growth and differentiation has long been appreciated by biologists. In general, cells that are dividing are unspecialized. In order for a cell to become differentiated, it apparently must stop dividing. It is as though a cell has limited resources and has the choice of either carrying out multiple syntheses associated with metabolism and cell division or synthesizing large amounts of a small number of substances.

All of the short-lived fixed postmitotics are highly specialized.

Epithelial cells may produce keratin, mucus, sebum, or other secretions, or may have special organelles such as cilia or flagella. Erythrocytes are filled with hemoglobin and have an unusual dumbbell shape. Granulocytic leukocytes contain high concentrations of lysosomes. Spermatazoa, which represent a special type of fixed postmitotic, in being haploid, are adapted for rapid motion and penetration of the egg.

These cells all have very short life spans. Populations age in the sense that, in most cases, the probability of dying increases with increasing time. A population of red blood cells that has been labeled during cell division in the bone marrow has a life span of around 120 days in the human being. The percent survival, or rate of dying, curve is typical of an aging population. In the dog, a similar curve showing red cell survival of around 110 days is obtained. In addition to disappearance of cells from the circulation due to senescence, cells are also removed at random in some species such as the rabbit and cat. Resulting survival curves are between the curves for a random hit process (first-order reaction) and the rectangular curve for an aging population.

Granulocytic leukocytes, on the other hand, appear to be removed from circulating blood and destroyed in a random fashion with a half time of around seven hours in the human being. This suggests that these cells are aged at the time they are released from bone marrow, in the sense that they are already unstable and that the rate of their destruction does not increase with increasing time. Circulating lymphocytes exist in two populations: small cells that survive over 90 days, and large lyphocytes with turnover time of around 60 days in the rat.

Death in epithelial cells is clearly age-related, since cells at the surface are the ones that die, and it takes time for cells to reach this site. As an example of the short life span of such cells, the epithelium of the gastrointestinal tract in man is turned over every 6 days.

The question arises as to whether or not there is a difference in life span of these short-lived cells in animals of different ages. This question has received little attention. The study mentioned earlier, in which erythrocytes from young and old animals were cross-transfused, indicated that there was no difference in survival time. In the case of intestinal epithelium, also discussed earlier, the data suggested that postmitotic cells survive slightly longer in older animals because of slower replacement from the progenitor pool.

What dying consists of varies from one cell type to another. In some glands, products of the cells replace other components and distend the cells until they rupture. In a stratified squamous epithelium, the cells become filled with keratin, which replaces all other components. Finally, such cells are sloughed from the surface as scales. Red blood cells fragment, and the fragments are taken up by cells of the reticuloendothelial system and degraded. The fate of granulocytes is uncertain, but they are probably destroyed shortly after removal from the circulation.

Death of leukocytes and epithelial cells has been observed in vitro. There is no single or characteristic change. The cell surface shows beading and pseudopod formation. Cells take up water. Some parts become more liquid, while other parts appear more gellike. Membranes rupture with the release of nuclear and cytoplasmic components. Vacuoles form in mitochondria, nuclei, and in the cytoplasm. These changes can be characterized as a generalized morphological degeneration.

Possible causes of death have not been systematically studied. In the previous chapter reference was made to studies suggesting that calcium accumulation might shorten life spans of nerve cells. Cause of death is a particularly difficult problem, since there is no simple way of distinguishing cause from effect when cell properties are found to be altered. It is often assumed that so many of the cell's resources are used in carrying out specialized functions that the cell is unable to renew enzymes necessary for life, or to generate high-energy compounds required for the maintenance of semipermeability of membranes and structural integrity of organelles. This would appear to be a reasonable hypothesis when one considers some extreme examples.

Cells in a keratinizing squamous epithelium become filled with keratin. Eventually all cellular components, including the nucleus, are replaced by this cell product. In the case of red cells, the cells are filled with hemoglobin and lose their nuclei. Reasons for an inability to carry out normal metabolic reactions in these cells are obvious. The same factors, although less striking, very likely operate in the other short-lived fixed postmitotics.

Since proliferating cells must synthesize all of the metabolic enzymes and organelles, this concept explains in a general way why differentiating cells lose their ability to divide. The question then becomes one of determining the factors that cause a cell either to synthesize a special component or to synthesize the spectrum of basic enzymes and macromolecules.

Synthesis of special products may explain evolution of cell populations that turn over. On the hypothesis that such synthesis leads to cell death, a mechanism must be available for the continuous replacement of dying cells.

Aging of long-lived fixed postmitotics

The full complement of these cells is present at around the time of birth. They do not divide and, in terms of end points, should be convenient systems for the study of cell aging if, in fact, they do age. Neurones and skeletal muscle constitute a significant proportion of the body mass. In view of the functions of the nervous and muscular systems, any progressive alterations in large numbers of cells in these systems would be likely to have profound consequences. Oocytes also serve as examples of this type of cell. The long-lived fixed postmitotics are also highly specialized, but not to the point at which they are unable to carry out basic metabolic and synthetic functions.

In the previous chapter we considered what is known about age-related changes in cell constituents. It is possible that progressive alterations in a cell might interfere with some cell functions while permitting the cell to survive. It is more likely, however, that if cell components are altered progressively in a population of cells, many of the cells will die. Rates of attaining the end point of death should then be of use in studying aging of these cells.

Oocytes begin to disappear from the ovary before birth. The disappearance seems to occur in a linear fashion until all of the ova are gone. Thus, some ova have life spans of several hours, whereas others survive close to 50 years in the case of human beings. The probability of dying is not related to cell age. A linear survival curve is most characteristic of deaths caused by some external factor rather than by aging or by intracellular accidents. An analogy would be an ocean liner starting out with a large number of chickens; each day a certain number of chickens is killed for food. Perhaps the survival of ova depends on their location in the ovary, in relation to blood supply, surface, or dense fibrous tissue.

Striated muscle cells are exceedingly responsive to functional demands. When a cell is not working it rapidly loses structural proteins, and the patterns of protein synthesis and degradation and of metabolism become altered. Excessive or prolonged work has opposite effects. The consequences of inactivity or work can be recognized grossly in a muscle by atrophy or hypertrophy. These changes do not depend on number of muscle cells, which do not divide, but rather on the number of myofibrils within a muscle cell. The lability of muscle cells makes it difficult to evaluate changes with time, since any changes noted may be due to extracellular factors and may not be both progressive and irreversible.

The strength of a skeletal muscle is clearly related to age. As an animal matures, the strength of a muscle increases. Maximum strength is attained in the young adult. After the age of 25 to 30 years in man, strength declines gradually in a somewhat linear fashion (Fig. 5.11). This appears to be associated with some degree of muscle atrophy, although there is great individual variation, and atrophy may not be universal within a population. It is not known to what extent age-

Back
N = ?

Mean two hands
N = ?

Both hands
N = ?

Back
N = ?

Mean two hands
N = ?

Both hands
N = ?

Stronger hand
N = 7015

Mean two hands
N = 6998

Pull
N = 6985

Thumb
N = 2510

Wrist extension
N = 1728

Wrist flexion
N = 1728

Hand
N = 3923

Back
N = 3079

Biceps
N = 3108

Hand
N = 327

Preferred hand
N = 552

Mean two hands
N = 165

Intervals equal 20% of maximum

Age

Fig. 5.11 Effect of age on strength of various human muscles. (From Rodahl and Issekutz. 1962. In Rodahl and Horvath [ed.] Muscle as a Tissue. McGraw-Hill, New York.)

changes in intracellular components described in the previous chapter might be responsible for this loss of function with age. As animals age, they undergo a generalized debility and progressive loss of activity, as will be considered in some detail. Muscle atrophy could be secondary to such generalized debility, as well as to environmental changes in the vascular-connective tissue systems, which will be discussed in a later section.

With regard to end points, muscle cells do not appear to die or drop out as a function of age. If any are lost, the number involved is probably quite trivial.

Cells of the central nervous system have received considerable attention because, as fixed postmitotic cells, they would be expected to undergo changes with age. Because of their key role in regulation, any changes might be of importance in aging of the whole animal. Most observations have dealt with the morphology of cell changes, as described in the previous chapter, and with loss of cells as a function of age. Very few studies of nerve cell function have been undertaken. It has been reported that conduction velocity of a nerve decreases by about 15% between 30 and 90 years of age in man. Such a change could be due to progressive alterations in cell components, to diminished functional demand, or to selection of slower nerve fibers because of dropping out of faster cells. This question will be considered again in the next chapter.

Numbers of nerve cells surviving as a function of age have been determined at different sites of the human cerebral cortex. There is some cell loss at all locations, with most change occurring in the external and internal granular layers. Most marked losses occur in the superior temporal gyrus and post central gyrus. As shown in Fig. 5.12, the most rapid loss occurs between birth and maturity; loss after maturity is very slight. It has been suggested that the reported loss of neurones during growth may be in part artifactual because of the diluting out of neurones by the growth of nonneuronal elements. The loss occurring after maturity is roughly linear with time, suggesting a role for external factors in causing cell death. In terms of end points, human neurones do not represent an aging population; in fact, the probability of dying is greater, the younger the cell. Aging processes in terms of function may be found to occur in these cells when the appropriate studies are undertaken.

Studies of laboratory animals support the view that nerve cells do not die from aging processes; when they die in measurable numbers, death is due either to accidents or external causes. If cell death is due to these nonprogrammed or extracellular causes, and the probability of dying is related neither to the age of the animal nor to the age of the cell, cell loss might not be detectable in a short-lived animal, since it may take 30 years for a measurable change to occur in such

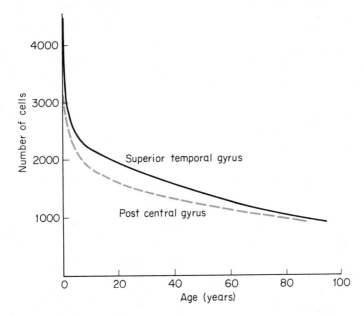

Fig. 5.12 Cell counts in the two areas of the human cerebral cortex which show the greatest change with age. (Drawn from data of Brody. 1955. J. Comp. Neurol. **102:**511.)

a cell population in human beings. Thus, no change in neurone density has been found with age in the rat cerebral cortex. Nor has an age-related change in numbers of rat sciatic nerve or ventral root fibers, or cat ventral root fibers been observed. Purkinje cells in the rat show a linear decline in number with age. In mice, nerve cells of the spinal cord are constant until 50 weeks of age, but show a 15 to 20% decrease by 110 weeks.

None of the populations of long-lived fixed postmitotics that have been studied gives a survival curve characteristic of an aging population. This suggests that there is no progressive intracellular process occurring that increases the probability of dying with increasing time. Intracellular changes described in the previous chapter may thus be of no consequence, or may result in functional debilities that are unrelated to cell viability. Loss of cells with time, regardless of mechanism, could, of course, cause aging phenomena at higher levels of organization in an animal.

Aging of cells in development

Many of the cell populations we have been discussing, if they change at all with age, appear to change most rapidly during the period of growth in the animal. Lag period before regeneration of liver, numbers of neurones, and generation time of intestinal epithelial cells become altered to the greatest extent between birth and maturity. Lymphoid organs such as thymus and tonsils are prominent in infancy, and become somewhat atrophic in the adults of many species. In addition, several organs that are hormone-dependent undergo atrophic changes as hormone patterns change at various times in the life of an animal. In these instances there is a decrease in cell number and in rate of cell division. These are all borderline aging processes, in that some criteria of an aging process appear to be satisfied, while in no case are all criteria known to be fulfilled.

These examples illustrate the difficulty at times of disentangling developmental from aging processes. In addition, a number of cell populations die out as parts of early developmental processes. In general, rates of dying of these cells are characteristic of aging populations. Zones of dead and dying cells can be identified at many sites in developing embryos and in metamorphosing animals. The losses of tails and gills in anurans, of Mullerian and Wolffian ducts, and of pronephros and mesonephros occur largely by cell death and dissolution. Whenever lumens form in tissues, or separation, fusion, or invagination occurs, cell death is extensive. When it has been studied, cell death has been seen to consist of a generalized deterioration, associated with the presence of high concentrations of lysosomal enzymes.

It is not known to what extent death in these cells is due to intrinsic aging processes, or to what extent to external influences. A number of studies have shown that genetic factors, as well as environmental conditions, play key roles in programmed cell death. Several mutants are known in which cell death does not occur. Such animals develop a variety of abnormalities in morphogenesis.

Grafting experiments have been of use in evaluating factors required for cell death. In sculpturing of the limb bud in the chick embryo, certain zones of cells die on schedule. If the presumptive necrotic zone is grafted onto somite tissue or placed in organ culture, the cells die at the usual time. If grafted to a site on the wing bud where necrosis does not occur, the cells survive and differentiate. It has been postulated that these cells will deteriorate and die when on their own; that they require some substance for survival which can be provided by cells in areas where degeneration does not occur.

Cell death in some cases is under hormonal control. The thyroid hormone accelerates degeneration of cells of gills, tail, and musculature in metamorphosis of tadpoles. In birds, involution of the Mullerian and Wolffian ducts is under the influence of testes and ovaries, respectively. Although treatment with androgens and estrogens can reproduce the gonadal effects, these hormones have not been shown to be present in significant concentrations in embryos. In mammals, the presence of testes is required for the degeneration of Mullerian ducts, while involution of Wolffian ducts appears more genetically determined and intrinsic; unless an ovary is present, Wolffian ducts degenerate.

Physical state of the immediate environment is important in at least one instance. In the formation of bone from cartilage there is a definite sequence in which cartilage cells mature, the extracellular matrix becomes mineralized, and the cells then die. If the matrix does not mineralize, as in vitamin D deficiency, the cells do not die. It has been suggested that mineralization of the matrix interferes with diffusion processes, and that the cells starve or accumulate toxic waste products.

Finally, the opportunity of a cell to function may determine whether or not it will survive. Spinal ganglia are all about the same size early in the embryo. As limbs differentiate, they are innervated by certain ganglia. In these ganglia, large numbers of neurones survive, while in other ganglia many of the cells die. With subsequent development, ganglia supplying limbs remain large, and ganglia not innervating limbs become small. Death of cells that have no function may explain losses of cells, which occur at a rapid rate in young animals.

Some judgments

When very complicated systems exist over long periods of time, a number of changes would be anticipated. It is a continuing problem to decide which changes are important, and which are trivial. From data available, it is often impossible to know if the changes represent aging changes in being universal, progressive, and irreversible. It is also usually impossible to tell whether the changes are intrinsic to the cell or are caused by environmental factors or control mechanisms.

An important change is one that causes an observable alteration in the function or properties of the system, or which answers a question that a student of the system thinks is worth asking. In terms of cell dynamics—the number present, rate of division, and generation time—changes over the life span of an animal appear trivial. In some populations, no changes in these parameters have been observed; in others, changes occur most rapidly during periods of maximum growth of the animal. It is possible that early in development, there is a great excess of cells in various populations. As growth and development proceed, there is a loss of some cells, by decreased cell division and by death of cells, so that only cells that are called upon to function are maintained. There may be a resorting of cell populations so that a steady state is achieved in the whole animal. Atrophy of nonfunctioning tissue and the death of unused neurones support this notion. It is necessary to consider age-changes in these cells, because we shall have to evaluate their role in aging at higher levels of organization. Even negative data may be of use in this connection.

As noted earlier, the aging of cells cultured under optimal conditions does not appear to serve as a model for any process occurring in a cell population in an animal. Differences in potential cell doublings between cells derived from fetal, embryonic, and cancer tissue may be more relevant to questions about growth cessation and neoplasia than about aging per se. On the other hand, the culture of explants and of cells in sera of different ages is probably of value in determining the effect of extracellular changes with age on cell proliferation and survival.

It has been more difficult to gain information on changes in cell function with age than on population dynamics. In the case of populations, many studies show no change, while some investigations indicate changes that occur most rapidly during rapid animal growth. A rare report describes significant enzyme variations between cells from adult and old animals. Such findings should be confirmed and extended, with particular reference to the criteria of universality, progression, and irreversibility.

It would be difficult to explain intrinsic age-changes in intermitotics, although some possibilities were mentioned in the previous chapter. Long-lived fixed postmitotics would be likely candidates for change, however—certainly in components which are metabolically inert. Some morphological changes with age were described in the previous chapter. It is not known if there are any functional consequences of these alterations. Function of these cells with increasing age has received very little attention. Changes in an organ such as muscle tell us only that some alterations have occurred; alterations could be in the muscle cells, extracellular material, blood vessels, nutritional state, or recent history of the muscle in terms of training and exercise. Such cells as muscle and neurones could become altered in their specialized function, in membrane properties, for example, without any significant change in metabolic and synthetic processes necessary for life.

Deterioration and death of the short-lived fixed postmitotics are clearly the result of aging processes. Aging of populations of these cells does not appear to be related in any significant way to the life span of the animal. They serve not only as examples of cell aging, but also as examples of systems in which differentiation occurs at the expense of cell growth and division. The interrelationship between development and aging in these cells is obvious.

Degeneration of cells in the developing animal demonstrates the type of programming that can occur in cell aging. Such programming may be intrinsic to the cells, or may reside in the environment or distant organs and probably has different bases in the case of different tissues. These cell populations also point out how various components of an organism can age independently of each other and of the aging of the entire animal. These populations age as the organism is growing and developing most rapidly.

Some useful studies

1. Activities of intermitotics from animals of different ages. Bone marrow cells or epithelial cells of various types could be studied with regard to enzyme content and rate of protein synthesis. Data from such cells after several passages in tissue culture, so that environmental effects were abolished, would be useful additions to the small amount of information we have on this problem.

2. Mechanism of death in short-lived fixed postmitotics. Permeability of membranes, ion, and enzyme content could be determined in these cells as they become specialized and die.

3. Role of animal growth and activity in cell population dynamics. By dietary means, animals could be made to grow slowly or rapidly. Animals could also be kept active by exercise, or inactive. Cell populations in the animals could be studied in terms of numbers of cells present, numbers of stem cells, and generation time. It would be of particular interest to see if slow growth and inactivity reproduced any of the effects seen with age, and if these were reversible. Similar animals would be of use in studying the enzyme content of cells and rates of protein synthesis, in view of the changes that have been reported in cells from animals of different ages.

4. Function of long-lived fixed postmitotics. Studies of single isolated neurones and muscle cells from individuals of different ages, in terms of membrane permeability, depolarization, and conduction velocity would be feasible. Such activities as flow of axoplasm in nerve fibers and contraction of myofibrils might also be investigated. Such studies would indicate whether or not significant changes occur in these cells. They could be followed up by studies of cells from active and inactive or growing and nongrowing animals to determine the effects of extrinsic factors.

REFERENCES

Biggers, J. D. 1964. The death of cells in normal multicellular organisms. *In* A. V. S. de Reuck and J. Knight [ed.], Cellular injury. Little, Brown & Co., Boston.

Brizzee, K. R., N. Sherwood, and P. S. Timiras. 1968. A comparison of cell populations at various depth levels in cerebral cortex of young adult and aged Long-Evans rats. J. Gerontol. 23:289.

Eadie, G. S. and I. W. Brown. 1953. Red blood cell survival studies. Blood. 8:1110.

Krohn, P. L. 1962. Heterochronic transplantation in the study of ageing. Proc. Roy. Soc. B. 157:128.

Mende, T. J. 1965. Studies on Cr^{51} labeled erythrocyte turnover in relation to age. Gerontologia. 11:57.

Pisciotta, A. V., D. W. Westring, C. DePrey, and B. Walsh. 1967. Mitogenic effect of phytohaemagglutinin at different ages (human). Nature. 215:193.

Saunders, J. W. 1966. Death in embryonic systems. Science. 154:604.

Wright, E. A. and J. M. Spink. 1959. A study of the loss of nerve cells in the central nervous system in relation to age. Gerontologia. 3:277.

Yuhas, J. M. and J. B. Storer. 1967. The effect of age on two modes of radiation death and on hematopoietic cell survival in the mouse. Radiat. Res. 32:596.

SIX

Aging of Animals:

Observations and

Questions

Aging usually denotes the phenomena or processes having to do with the deterioration and dying out of members of a population of animals in a highly predictable fashion with the passage of time. The fact that these changes in populations occur in such a predictable fashion tells us that aging is as much a part of normal biology as growth and differentiation, and also indicates that changes with profound consequences must be occurring at the molecular and tissue levels.

Although we are now considering aging of animals, we know from previous discussions that aging processes occur at a variety of levels, from extracellular molecules to populations of cells. Some of these systems clearly age independently of aging of the animals that contain them, whereas changes in some systems are related to the life span of the animal. We have essentially surveyed changes with age at molecular and cell levels up to this point. A number of age-related alterations have been described and, where information is lacking, we have suggested possibilities and indulged in some speculations. Basic causes of animal aging most likely reside in some tissue changes that have already been discussed or postulated.

The single most important goal in the study of aging is to understand aging of an intact animal in terms of molecular and tissue events. Before we return to a consideration of aging at these basic levels, it is necessary to consider what phenomena in aging animals must be explained by basic changes—in short, what is meant specifically by aging of an animal? When we know what must be explained—what types of questions to ask—we shall have some meaningful frames of reference for evaluation of the roles of tissue and molecular changes.

This chapter will deal with manifestations of aging—how aging is identified, described, and defined in an animal. Inferences are frequently made from life table data—from rates and probabilities of dying in a population. It is necessary, however, to know what changes are progressing before the end point of death. For this reason, references will often be made to human populations. Man leaves much to be desired as an experimental animal. However, he is most useful for the study of aging; so much is known about rates of dying, causes of death, and metabolic and physiological changes over the life span in very large human populations. Heterogeneity of populations and environmental variations are frequently advantageous, because the role of these factors can be evaluated; the experiments have been performed by nature. In recent years considerable information has accumulated on disease incidence and physiological changes in aging laboratory animals. Studies of these populations are becoming increasingly useful.

The dying out of populations

In Ch. 1 it was pointed out that populations dying out can be described by two extreme types of curve: the logarithmic die-away or first-order reaction rate curve for populations in which deaths are due to accidents or non-age-related causes, and the rectangular curve for populations in which deaths are due to aging. When percentage surviving is plotted as a function of age for animal populations, curves between these two extremes are obtained. We can then compare populations in terms of relative influences of accidental and age-related causes of death.

Figure 6.1 shows survival curves for a number of human populations. Shapes of the curves are dependent on standard of living and technological attainments of the various societies. Population density, sanitation, nutrition, and public health measures such as immunization programs and use of antibiotics play key roles in determining the shape of these curves. In underdeveloped societies there are large numbers of non-age-related deaths, or deaths that occur predominantly in young individuals. Most of these deaths are from infectious disease. As societies become more advanced, survival curves become more rectangular. In the most highly developed cultures, the curve becomes that of an aging population; most deaths are results of aging processes.

It can be seen from these curves that the maximum life span of 90 to

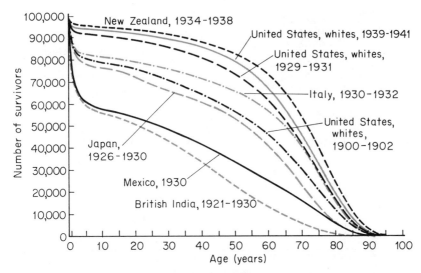

Fig. 6.1 Survival curves for various human populations. (From Comfort. 1956. The Biology of Senescence. Holt, Rinehart, and Winston, Inc., New York.)

95 years is about the same in the different societies. This tells us that technological and medical progress have had no effect on human life span as an intrinsic characteristic of populations. What has been changed is the probability of dying in younger age groups. In modern societies more individuals can expect to live out the human life span. Life expectancy at birth has increased, while life expectancy at 65 to 70 years of age has remained quite constant in western societies since data of this type have been recorded.

We also know from these curves that as research on specific diseases leads to effective means of prevention or treatment, the survival curve will become slightly more rectangular, with no change in maximum survival. In other words, the human life span will not be altered until underlying causes of aging are slowed or inhibited. In fact, most of the non-age-related diseases involving large numbers of people have already been dealt with rather successfully in the most advanced societies. Life expectancy at birth has changed very little in the last decade or so in these populations.

If different inbred strains of mice are looked after very well and, in particular, are protected from epidemics, a family of survival curves is obtained (Fig. 6.2). All of these curves are somewhat rectangular, indicating that most deaths in all of the strains are age-related. It might appear that some strains age sooner than others. It turns out, however, that the short-lived strains are highly susceptible to certain fatal diseases. Virtually all individuals of strain AKR/J, for example,

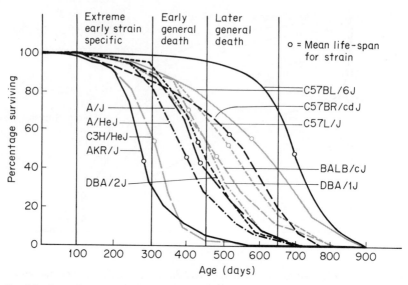

Fig. 6.2 Survival curves for mice of various inbred strains. (From Biology of the Laboratory Mouse by The Staff of the Jackson Laboratory. Copyright © 1966 by McGraw-Hill, Inc. Used with permission of McGraw-Hill Book Company.)

develop leukemia and die at an early age. In such a population the onset and progression of leukemia could be considered aging processes. This disease would represent an aging process only in those members of the population that were destined to die from it. The mouse strains susceptible to certain diseases have been selectively bred for this reason. The characteristic survival curve for the mouse as a species would probably be that for strain C57BL/6J. These animals die from a variety of age-related causes.

An important way of characterizing an aging population in terms of end points was discovered by Gompertz, an English actuary, in 1825. He found that after maturity, the rate and probability of dying are exponential with increasing age. If the life span is divided into short intervals, and the percentage of those alive at the beginning of each interval that die during the interval is plotted as a function of age, an exponential curve is obtained. If the logarithm of the mortality rate, or age-specific death rate, is plotted, a straight line is obtained (Fig. 6.3). This tells us that rate and probability of dying double at regular intervals.

In the first chapter it was pointed out that if a homogeneous population dies out because of aging, and if life span has an approximately normal distribution, then the age-specific death rate becomes exponential after the mean life span. In real populations the mortality curve becomes exponential much earlier in life. This is because life

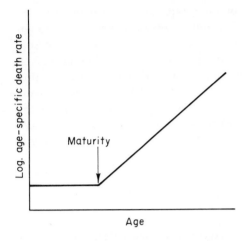

Fig. 6.3 Rate and probability of dying as a function of age (Gompertz plot).

span has a skewed rather than a normal distribution; more individuals die at earlier ages than would be the case if all died from the same age-related causes. Figure 6.4 shows the distribution of life spans for

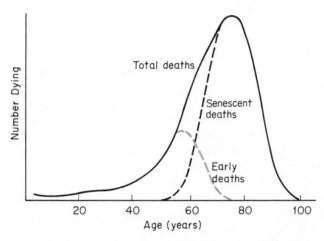

Fig. 6.4 Distribution of deaths in a human population. (Redrawn from Benjamin. 1959. *In* Ciba Foundation Colloquia on Ageing. Vol. 5. J. & A. Churchill, London.)

a human population. The curve for total deaths can be resolved into two curves: a normal distribution curve for that segment of the population that is rather homogeneous in dying off because of a small number of age-related processes, and a second curve for a heterogeneous population in which members die from non-age-related, or partially age-related causes, and as consequences of agelike changes occurring only in certain subgroups.

Life span and survival data of these types have a number of uses. They indicate the extent to which end points of aging are characteristic of populations, and demonstrate that these end points are programmed and predictable. They can frequently tell us whether a given population is aging or not. Most importantly, they give an indication of what types of phenomena must be explained by changes at tissue and molecule levels. Progressive alterations must be occurring in the tissues to cause end points of death. A consideration of mechanisms of death will enable us to be more specific in trying to relate tissue changes to mortality data.

Diseases and aging

It is not always easy to determine cause of death, even after a very careful post mortem examination. Frequently, the lesions noted do not appear severe enough to cause death, or no significant lesions are found, or there are so many different kinds of disease processes present in an individual that it is difficult to decide which was the primary cause and which were contributing causes of death. The latter difficulty, in particular, holds for individuals in old populations. When a number of severe diseases are present, it appears fortuitous that one kills rather than another. When very large populations are considered, however, it is likely that errors in judgment and observation would cancel each other out, and that an approximation of the truth would be achieved.

In Fig. 6.5 the age-specific death rate for the most important diseases and accepted causes of death has been plotted as a function of age for the United States population. In this semilog plot, the curve for all deaths is a straight line in accord with the Gompertz function; the probability of dying doubles about every eight years after maturity.

The majority of deaths are due to a rather small number of pathologic processes: arteriosclerosis, hypertension, and malignant neoplasms. The role of age in determining these end points can be evaluated by noting if the curve for a given cause of death is parallel to or rises faster than the all-causes curve or if it falls away from the all-deaths curve with increasing age. Deaths due to arteriosclerosis, which includes arteriosclerotic heart disease, most vascular diseases of the central nervous system, and the majority of chronic renal diseases, are clearly age-dependent. The curve for hypertension similarly parallels the all-causes curve, although very late in the life span it drops away slightly. Respiratory infections, such as influenza and pneumonia, and accidents become more age-dependent with increasing age, so that curves for these end points rise faster than the all-deaths curve in the later decades of life. This indicates that basic aging processes

Fig. 6.5 Mortality from selected causes by age. (From Kohn. 1963. J. Chron. Dis. 16:5.)

increase the susceptibility to death from these causes faster than the probability of dying from more common causes of death increases. On the other hand, the curve for malignant neoplasms drops away from the all-causes curve in later decades. This tells us that the probability of dying from a neoplasm does not increase as fast as the probability of dying, and that neoplasms affect only a certain segment of the population. As this segment dies off, the probability in the entire population of becoming afflicted rises at a lower rate or declines. The divergence of such a curve from the Gompertz function is characteristic of those diseases that are either present or absent, rather than present to some degree in all, and which are either cured or rapidly prove fatal. Many diseases in this category, syphilis for example, are only very peripherally related to aging processes.

These mortality curves can be used for calculating what would happen if some present efforts in biomedical research were wholly successful. If no one died from cancer, the all-causes curve would be replaced by the ALL-NEOPL. curve, and life expectancy at birth would be increased by about two years. If arteriosclerosis were conquered, the all-causes curve would become ALL-AS, and about seven more years of life would be expected. A population free of these two major diseases would gain 9 to 10 years of life (curve ALL-AS-NEOPL.). What diseases would then kill the population? Deaths would be due to the miscellaneous group of other diseases—particularly respiratory infections and accidents, which increase so rapidly as causes of death in the older populations. In fact, from extrapolating the curves for influenza and pneumonia and accidents, it would appear that the population free of cancer and arteriosclerosis would be cut down very quickly, and that the estimated increase of 9 to 10 years is probably overoptimistic. This bears out the earlier assertion that progress in research on specific diseases might make the survival curve more rectangular but would not lengthen life span by very much.

The diseases with which large numbers of aging individuals die can be classified in three ways in regard to aging. One category consists of diseases that are aging processes themselves. These diseases occur in all members of the population, and are progressive and irreversible under usual conditions. Arteriosclerosis is a good example of such a disease. A variety of factors, nutritional, metabolic, and genetic, and the presence of other diseases influence the rate of progression of arteriosclerosis. However, the essential fact of this disease is that it consists of a chronic inflammatory reaction in the walls of arteries, characterized by the proliferation of small vessels, the accumulation of minerals, lipids and glycoproteins, and by scarring associated with the formation of large amounts of collagen. Many of these changes occur diffusely through the vessels, but at certain sites they are severe enough to cause the formation of plaques. This disease progresses in everyone. Figure 6.6 compares aortas from a young adult and an old individual. Those who die do so from complications: growth of a plaque, or hemorrhage within a plaque so that the lumen is occluded, or from a blood clot forming on the plaque.

Hypertension, or increased blood pressure, takes several forms. One

Fig. 6.6 Opened aortas from adult (left) and old (right) human beings.

type, secondary to increasing rigidity of the large arteries, represents an aging process in that it occurs in all members of the population, although there is considerable individual variation in rate of progression. Other types of hypertension are caused by increased peripheral resistance to blood flow, secondary to altered reactivity, or increased rigidity of arterioles. There are several etiologies involved, and the role of age is somewhat obscure. Although increased peripheral resistance occurs with age in a large fraction of the population, it does not occur in all. It appears that several subgroups are involved and, depending on etiology, the incidence of hypertension increases at different rates as a function of age. This brings us to the second way of classifying diseases.

The second category of diseases consists of those diseases which do not occur in all members of the population, but which show an increasing incidence as the population ages. These diseases do not, in the strictest sense, represent aging processes, because the criterion of universality is not satisfied. If, however, only the population destined to develop such a disease or to die from it is considered, the disease

113

becomes an aging process for that population. Many, if not most diseases, can be considered in these terms. Progressive muscular dystrophy of childhood, for example, is fatal for essentially the entire afflicted population by the age of 20 years. If only this population were being observed, the mortality data would be those of an aging population with a maximum life span of around 20 years. Most of these diseases are not relevant to a consideration of aging of the entire population, or of aging as a normal biological process. Some of these diseases must be considered, however, because their incidence does increase exponentially, or at least very rapidly in the later decades of life, and because they play some role in determining the shape of the survival curve.

The increasing incidence of certain types of hypertension is an example of this class of diseases. Perhaps the best example is malignant neoplasms. Malignancies as a whole, as cause of death, parallel the all-deaths curve, or rise faster over part of the life span, but then drop away in the last decades (Fig. 6.5). Reasons for the varying shape of this curve can be appreciated when mortality data for different types of tumors are examined.

Figure 6.7 shows the age-specific death rates for certain selected tumors. Cancer of the colon is quite common, and appears to represent an aging process to the extent that the incidence increases with increasing age, and the increase is more rapid with increasing age. The curve suggests that all might get this cancer if they lived long enough. On the other hand, deaths due to cancer of lung and kidney drop off late in life. If an individual has not developed cancer of the lung by around 70 years of age, or of kidney by 82 years, the probability of getting these cancers drops off significantly in succeeding years. In addition, it is seen that there is a risk of kidney cancer in childhood that disappears by about 12 years. This is due to a specific kind of embryonal kidney tumor. Similarly, there is a maximum risk of death due to bone tumors at around 13 years. This is due to two special types of bone neoplasms. The remaining curve for bone tumors is irregular because of specific types of tumors that have characteristic age-incidences. Leukemia also exists in a childhood form, and in forms that show a strong age-dependent incidence.

Some of these tumors clearly occur in only a segment of the population. Others might eventually occur in all, but this cannot be ascertained because the entire population dies off while the incidence is still rising. Although all criteria of an aging process are not satisfied by malignant neoplasms, the obviously important role of age in determining incidences justifies an attempt to understand the types of age-related molecular and tissue events that might be responsible.

A neoplastic disease occurs in several stages; neoplastic transformation of cells is followed by growth and tissue invasion, spread and

Fig. 6.7 Age-specific death rates for several neoplasms: Colon, lung, and leukemia per 10⁶ people, bone and kidney per 10⁷ people. (From U.S. Vital Statistics, 1965.)

metastasis to distant sites, and growth and invasion at these sites. The course of a neoplastic disease depends on properties of the malignant cells and on a number of poorly defined host factors that influence the viability, spread, and invasive capacity of tumors.

Roles of age in the various phases of neoplasia have been studied in experimental animals by the induction and transplantation of tumors.

Many of the most conspicuous age differences occur between birth and maturity. Thus, weanling or very young animals are more susceptible than mature animals to viral-induced leukemia, the mammary tumor agent, and to the induction of liver tumors by urethane. The growth of a transplanted rat sarcoma is greatest in newborn animals, and drops to a low level at about the time of weaning. On the other hand, the effectiveness of estrogen treatment in causing development of leukemia in mice appears greatest at around the time of sexual maturity.

Several reports indicate that changes after maturity favor the spread and growth of tumors. Older animals develop more metastases than young after the injection of ascites tumor cells. Certain human tumors have been successfully transplanted to old, but not to mature mice. It has been reported that transplanted lymphosarcomas grow better in old animals, whereas liver tumors do better in younger animals; the growth of skeletal muscle tumors is unrelated to age.

Many of the results quoted in experimental neoplasia studies may be due to changes over the life span in endocrine status and in immunological competence. Immaturity of immune mechanisms in very young animals may be of particular importance in tumor induction. The role of immune reactions in "spontaneous" tumors is controversial at present, and the problem is further complicated by results of transplantation experiments. The relevance of animal experiments to relationships between age and neoplasia in natural populations is uncertain. Perhaps the appropriate generality is that age-related factors appear to be of importance in the various stages of experimentally induced and transplanted neoplastic diseases, and that studies of possible underlying aging processes are required.

The third category of diseases is diseases that do not occur in all, and which do not show very consistent age-related incidences, but which, when they occur, have more serious consequences, the older the individual. It is this miscellaneous group of diseases and insults, particularly accidents and respiratory infections, which perhaps best characterizes the relationship between age and disease. It has been seen to what extent these diseases would cause a Gompertz-type mortality curve in the absence of certain diseases that now cause the majority of deaths in a human population.

Bronchopneumonia occurs at all ages. As individuals become older, however, and particularly if they have some debilitating illness or have experienced some trauma such as an accident or surgery, they frequently develop pneumonia and die. What is of interest in regard to aging processes is that the tissue damage from the pneumonia may be very slight. Young individuals with the same degree of lung involvement would quickly recover. In other words, basic aging processes are occurring which decrease the probability of surviving rather trivial insults. This age-related decrease in resistance holds for a variety of infections and for internal accidents such as hernias, intestinal obstructions, and ulcers.

These diseases, which are responsible for the doubling of rate of dying every 8 years, and which enable us to characterize a human population as an aging one, have little relationship to one another in terms of development and progression of specific lesions. Thus, an arteriosclerotic plaque, cancer of the colon, rigid arteriole, lung infection, and hernia appear to have little to do with each other. Yet, as causes of death in the later decades of the human lifespan, they all increase more or less exponentially. It should also be noted that many individuals have these diseases concurrently, and that it is often fortuitous that one is a cause of death rather than another. This information gives rise to the concept that there may be one or a small number of basic aging processes in tissues which cause or predispose to all of these diseases. Aging processes would then constitute a 100 percent fatal disease that everyone has. The age-related diseases could then be viewed as complications.

This view is supported by plots of frequency distributions of deaths from different causes. Modal values for age of death from such apparently unrelated causes as cardiovascular-renal disease, pneumonia and influenza, and accidents (female) are 79–81 years (Fig. 6.8). The life span for man as a species thus appears to be around 80 years. Other causes of death in Fig. 6.8 are those diseases in which incidence increases as a function of age. Populations with these diseases do not live out the full life span.

Less is known about causes of death in aging animals other than man. However, the same generalities applied to human diseases will also hold for laboratory animals undergoing natural aging; in simple terms, the probability of dying doubles at regular intervals, and if an individual does not die from one disease, it will die from another. Diseases of animals may also be categorized in the same three ways in relationship to age. In Fig. 6.9 the incidences of the most common diseases in a strain of laboratory rat are plotted as a function of age; infections and certain neoplasms that also occur in this strain are excluded. The presence of these diseases is determined by examination of tissues and, although the data of Fig. 6.9 might give the impression that the lesions are all-or-none phenomena in individuals, some of them represent aging processes, since they occur in all members of the population. They are recognized, however, only when a certain level of severity is attained. Thus, chronic nephrosis and muscular

Fig. 6.8   Deaths from principal causes in a human population. (Louis I. Dublin, Alfred J. Lotka, and Mortimer Spiegelman. Length of Life—A Study of the Life Table, revised edition. Copyright 1949, The Ronald Press Company, New York.)

degeneration are aging processes because they eventually affect the entire population. The other diseases afflict only a fraction of the population, but are clearly age-dependent. In animals, more often than in

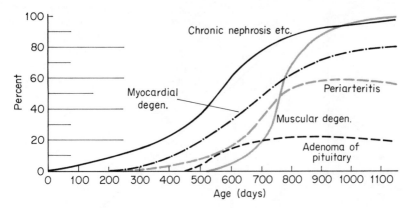

Fig. 6.9   Percent incidence of major lesions in rats as a function of age. (From Simms. 1965. Aging and Levels of Biological Organization. Univ. of Chicago Press, Chicago. © 1965 by the University of Chicago.)

man, cause of death cannot be determined. Many older animals that die show minimal tissue changes. This indicates the increasing probability of dying from trivial insults, or the decreasing efficiency of resistance factors with age.

The lesions commonly identified in aging rats and mice, in addition to infections and tumors, are inflammations of small vessels, hypertension, chronic inflammatory reactions of kidneys, and scarring of the heart muscle.

When attempting to evaluate various basic processes in regard to their possible importance in the actual aging of an animal, it would be difficult to take any process seriously that could not explain the development and progression of diseases that are responsible for the increasing probability of dying of a population.

Age and responses to stress

Declining resistance to stress in the form of disease is one of the most characteristic features of an aging population. This has been studied more directly by subjecting animals of various ages to controlled stresses, and observing their capacity to react or compensate in terms of some end point, usually death.

When mice were cold-stressed by being placed at temperatures of 6 to 7°C for 14 days, the percentage surviving decreased linearly with age (Fig. 6.10). What is really being measured here is the ability of animals to keep warm. The production and conservation of body heat depend on a large number of metabolic and physiologic processes. It

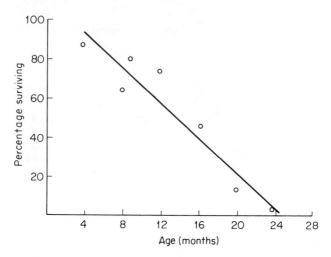

Fig. 6.10   Percentage of mice surviving 6–7°C for 14 days as a function of age. (Redrawn from Trujillo, et al. 1962. Radiat. Res. **16**:144.)

is of interest that the survival curve is linear with age, rather than showing an increasing rate of dying, or an increasingly negative slope, as would be seen in the case of a natural stress such as pneumonia. This suggests that either the severity or incidence of such a natural stress increases with age. On the other hand, the linear decline is quite characteristic for loss of function, as will be dealt with in a later section.

It has been possible to gain estimates of the actual ability to react to stress as a function of age. Mice of various ages were forced to do continuous work at elevated temperature to the limit of their endurance. The end point was the onset of convulsions. Physiological capacitance in terms of gram calorie expenditure could be determined for each mouse. As shown in Fig. 6.11, physiological capacitance increases during maturation and then undergoes a linear decline with age.

It can be seen that if a certain output of energy or level of performance is required in order to maintain life in the face of stresses that are relatively constant over the life span, then the percentage unable to survive will increase with increasing age. Or the amount of stress required to kill an animal will decrease with increasing age. Results of many different types of experiments support this concept. Thus, if animals are bled and the amount of blood that must be lost in order for death to occur is determined as a function of age, it is found that the blood loss required drops off linearly with age after maturity (Fig. 6.12); the older the animal, the less the blood loss which can be tolerated.

Fig. 6.11 Physiological capacitance as a function of age in mice. (Redrawn from Hensley, et al. 1964. J. Gerontol. **19:317**.)

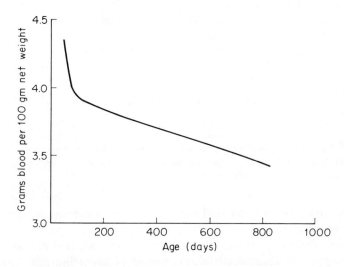

Fig. 6.12 Blood loss required to cause death of rats, as a function of age. (Redrawn from Simms. 1942. J. Gen. Physiol. **26:169**.)

The curve of Fig. 6.12 represents a quantity, and is linear with age. Such data, including standard deviations at each age, can be used to calculate probability of dying from a given blood loss as a function of age. These calculations have yielded a log, or Gompertzian mortality curve.

As a final example, we can consider the survival time of mice exposed to a standard daily dose of X-rays. Ionizing radiation is not an ideal injurious agent for a study of the role of aging in reaction to stress, because dividing cells are more sensitive to irradiation than resting ones, and young, growing animals contain more dividing cells than old animals. Mean survival time of mice did not change very conspicuously with age, as would be expected, since any generalized decreased resistance secondary to age might be balanced off by an increased cellular resistance. However, a very striking age-related increase in variance in survival time was observed (Fig. 6.13). This means that

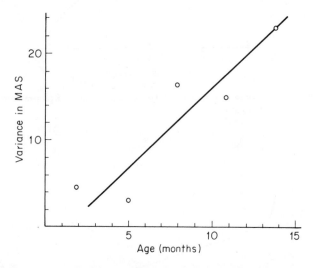

Fig. 6.13 Variance in survival time, under 100 r per day, in mice as a function of age. (Redrawn from Storer. 1965. Aging and Levels of Biological Organization. Univ. of Chicago Press, Chicago. © 1965 by the University of Chicago.)

as a population ages, the individuals become increasingly different from one another.

This increase in variance has been noted in several different types of measurements, such as barbiturate toxicity, body weight, and cardiac lipofuscin concentration. It is as though young animals are uniformly programmed, but that with age there is a progressive randomization within the population. This suggests that rates of aging are influenced to some extent by individual life histories, although it would be difficult to explain how a highly inbred mouse strain caged under very uniform conditions could contain individuals with different histories.

Some variance might be explained on the basis of an increase with age in the amplitude of fluctuations of a component or property. Sampling or measuring at a given time might then give greater variation in an aging population.

There are certain types of stresses to which animals might develop resistance as they become older. Cell resistance to radiation could be an example of this. Another might be certain infectious agents to which immunity is lacking in very young animals, but to which the adult population may be resistant. However, if we restrict our consideration to changes occurring after maturity, it is probably safe to predict that any stress or insult capable of killing an animal will kill an increasing percentage of the population as the population becomes older. Or as animals become older, stresses of decreasing magnitude will be required to cause death.

In summary, one category of causes of death, and that most characteristic of an aging population, is the miscellaneous group of diseases that kill off the population at a logarithmic rate as a function of age because of a decline in resistance factors. These experiments done by nature have been reproduced in the laboratory using controlled stresses of various kinds. To be able to explain the progressive decline in resistance factors in terms of cell and tissue changes is a major goal in aging research. We know enough already to go beyond the general concept of declining resistance factors, and can now consider those reactions and mechanisms that are responsible for maintaining resistance and steady states.

Physiologic processes and homeostatic mechanisms

The internal conditions under which life can exist are very restricted. Living processes within an animal are possible only within very narrow temperature and pH ranges, and only in the presence of a very delicate balance of ions, both intracellular and extracellular. Levels of nutrients, hormones, gases, and metabolites must not vary beyond rather close limits. A healthy animal maintains homeostasis, or relatively constant internal environment, under a variety of circumstances—at rest, or in a rapidly changing external environment, or during severe alterations in activity and feeding cycles.

If we were to observe any isolated component or property of the internal environment, we would find that it does not remain constant, but is continually undergoing fluctuations or perturbations around some mean value. Each factor is under control of several governors, as it were. Whenever deviation in one direction occurs, a control mechanism acts to make the factor return, so that there is a resulting over-shoot in the other direction, at which time another control mechanism begins to act, and so on. These governors or control mechanisms are all of the body's physiological processes.

Studies of the efficiency of physiological processes as a function of age have been very informative. The pattern that has emerged is one of an increasing sluggishness and inefficiency of all processes. Figure 6.14 contains data for function of the heart, kidney, and lungs.

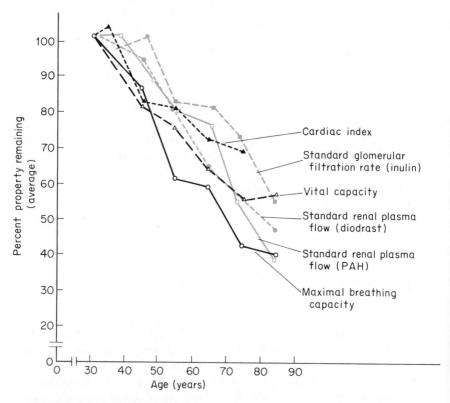

Fig. 6.14 Efficiency of human physiological mechanisms as a function of age. Level at 30 years is assigned a value of 100%. (Modified from Shock. 1960. Biology of Aging. American Institute of Biological Sciences, Washington, D.C.)

Although there is considerable individual variation at each age in measurement of function of these organ systems, which is not shown in the figure, it can be seen that function of these vital organs drops off linearly with age after maturity.

The decline in physiological efficiency with age applies to all systems.

In the previous chapter the decline in muscle strength was illustrated. Declines in hearing ability and in accommodation of the eye have frequently been documented. In the eye, also, transparency of the lens declines, and its refractive properties become altered with age. The ability of the stomach to secrete acid in response to food intake diminishes linearly with age (Fig. 6.15).

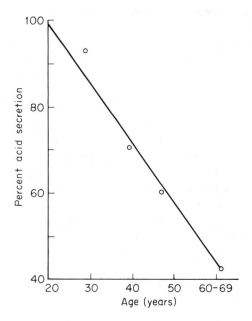

Fig. 6.15 Acid secretion in response to a test meal as a function of age of human males. (Redrawn from Ivy and Grossman. 1952. Problems of Aging. The Williams and Wilkins Co., Baltimore.)

Any number of examples could be given. It is probably safe to state that the ability of *every* organ or organ system to function declines progressively with age. This declining efficiency may be observed in some cases only when the system is stressed. Resting body temperature, for example, is the same in old and young animals. However, it was pointed out earlier that with age, animals are less able to produce and conserve heat when cold-stressed. Or when animals are maintained at elevated temperature, old animals show a greater rise in body temperature. Similarly, blood sugar levels are comparable in healthy young and old animals, but when sugar is administered, the rise in the blood concentration is greater in older animals, and more time is required for the drop to resting levels. The same applies to blood pH, which is the same in young and old, but which shows a greater rise in old animals in response to an alkali stress, and takes longer to return to the optimal level.

We can now appreciate the meaning of the decline in resistance factors, and can understand how older animals might die from insults that they would have survived at an earlier age. The important concept here is that this progressive sluggishness of physiological processes occurs throughout the body; changes cannot be ascribed to a single organ or organ system. This means that we will eventually want to consider tissues common to all organs.

Measurements of physiological processes in an animal are rather gross assessments of the consequences of processes occurring at molecular and tissue levels. Although there is an enormous number of physiological processes that can be measured, these depend on a small number of different types of reactions at the microscopic level. One type of reaction is cell and membrane movement. All physiological processes depend to some extent on the ability of such tissue as lung or blood vessel wall to dilate and to contract, and on the contraction and relaxation of smooth muscle cells in walls of arterioles. A second type of reaction that plays a role in most physiological processes is the passage, or transport of substances across membranes, from vessel to cell, or from cell to cell through the extracellular compartment. The elastic or contractile properties of tissues and the transport of substances within the body are determined largely by reactions of the vascular system, and the passage of materials is frequently affected by local states of dilatation or contraction, as in the case of gas diffusion in the lung, where transfer can occur efficiently only when alveoli are open.

The heart, of course, is the major contractile structure, and its function as a pump, regardless of the method of measurement used, declines in efficiency with age. Cardiac output declines about 0.7% per year. The amount of work performed per heart beat similarly drops off at a rate of about 1.0 percent per year.

When the heart contracts, the blood surges into the aorta, causing it to dilate. Energy of the stroke volume is then stored temporarily in the aorta. As the heart relaxes, the aorta contracts, driving the blood into the distal circulation. As the pressure wave travels down the aorta, it undergoes an amplification. The amount of this amplification between the aortic arch and iliac artery has been studied as a function of age in living human subjects. As shown in Fig. 6.16, the amplification drops off very markedly in a linear fashion with age. This has been attributed to a progressive loss in distensibility of peripheral vessels. In an independent study it was calculated that total peripheral resistance to blood flow increased 1.7 percent per year.

The distensibility of human thoracic aortas was studied directly by measuring the volume increase due to a constant inside pressure of 100 mm Hg, which is a pressure within the normal or physiological range. The distensibility fell off very markedly with increasing age

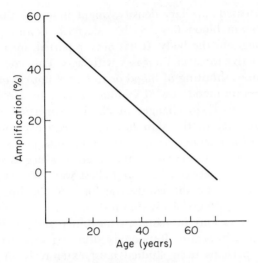

Fig. 6.16 Amplification of aortic pressure wave between aortic arch and iliac artery as a function of age in human beings. (Redrawn from O'Rourke, et al. 1968. Circ. Res. 23:567.)

(Fig. 6.17). By 85 years of age the aorta took on the elastic properties of a rigid tube. Such increasing stiffness of vessels has been observed in several peripheral arterial beds as well.

The combination of decreasing cardiac efficiency and increasing rigidity of the arterial system results in a diminished or sluggish tissue perfusion. The decreased renal plasma flow shown in Fig. 6.14 is a good example of this. It is not known to what extent other factors,

Fig. 6.17 Volume increase of human thoracic aorta under standard pressure as a function of age. (Redrawn from Bader. 1967. Circ. Res. 20:354.)

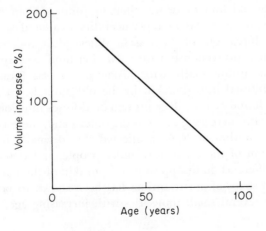

such as a decreased capillary density, might influence this age-related decrease in organ blood flow. Such a decrease is also probably not uniform throughout the body. It has been reported, for example, that blood flow in the forearm increases with age. This could be due to an arterio-venous shunting of blood or to loss of muscle tone with age. Further studies on blood flow at various sites are required.

Other tissues undergo changes in elastic properties with age. An increasing flaccidity of the skin has been frequently observed. The lung has a normal tendency to contract because of its elasticity. It is kept expanded by the chest, so that there is a negative pressure in the potential space between lung and chest wall. With age this negative pressure decreases; the contractile force of the lung, due to its intrinsic elasticity, progressively diminishes.

Studies of alterations in tissue permeability and in diffusion processes have scarcely begun. Pulmonary diffusing capacity of gases in the lung has perhaps been studied most extensively in this regard. There is a progressive loss in diffusing capacity amounting to about 8 percent per decade in human beings. It has been assumed that this is due to increasing membrane resistance, since total lung volume and number of alveoli have not been shown to change with age. A possibility that has not been excluded is a decreasing density of lung capillaries.

The age-related decrease in glomerular filtration rate shown in Fig. 6.14 represents a decline in diffusion, but, because of the complex capillary-membrane-cell relationships, the site of the alteration cannot be ascertained.

A number of other isolated studies have been undertaken. When labeled albumin was injected into dogs, it was found that with increasing age, less of the albumin had diffused from the circulation into the extravascular compartment of the heart. A saline solution injected into the skin has been reported to take longer to be absorbed in the case of old human beings than in young. When histamine is injected into the skin, vascular permeability is altered so that serum proteins can diffuse out of the vessels. When adult and old rats, previously injected intravenously with a dye that binds to serum proteins, were injected intradermally with histamine, it was found that less bound dye diffused into the skin in the old animals. In an in vitro study, it was found that a silver proteinate diffuses into joint cartilage more slowly with increasing age. On the other hand, there is one report that when a solution of Na^{22} is injected intradermally it disappears faster from skin of the forearm of older people, and that there is no age-related difference in disappearance from skin of the hand and face. Also, isolated strips of aortic intima has been shown to become more permeable to several small molecules with increasing age.

For any organ in which blood circulation or perfusion rate becomes sluggish with age, and in which permeability is altered, it would be possible to explain a decline in its functional efficiency with age. Such alterations would also be of use to us in that they would indicate that we must search for molecular and tissue changes with age which could explain them. It is obvious that many more systematic studies are required to demonstrate, organ by organ and tissue by tissue, changes with age in vascular dynamics and permeability.

Aging in the abstract: a model

Aging populations die out according to the Gompertz function; the age-specific death rate is exponential, whereas losses of physiological function appear to take place linearly. There have been several attempts to gain insight into how a linear decline in function could result in an exponential rate of dying, and how these phenomena might be altered in different populations and environments. These attempts have resulted in the construction of theoretical models of aging populations. It was pointed out earlier in this chapter that by calculations employing the standard deviation at each age in the measure of a quantity that falls off linearly—in that case, the amount of blood loss required to cause death—the probability of dying from a standard blood loss is found to increase according to the Gompertz function. We shall now examine a second model—the Strehler-Mildvan theory.

This theory is based on the concept that an organism is composed of systems whose functions are continually being displaced by randomly occurring internal and environmental stresses. The systems must do work in order to reestablish a steady state. The maximum rates at which these systems can expend energy constitute the viability of the organism. Death occurs when the demands on one or more systems surpass their ability to expend energy.

The theory assumes that the demands for energy are due to random fluctuations in the internal or external environment, and that the magnitudes of these stresses have a distribution similar to the distribution of kinetic energy of gas molecules according to the Maxwell-Boltzmann equation.

The Gompertz function can be expressed as:

$$R_m = R_0 e^{at}$$

where R_m is the mortality rate at time t, R_0 is the rate at birth, and a is a constant. R_0 is obtained by extrapolating the exponential curve back to zero time and does not truly represent the mortality rate at birth, because Gompertzian kinetics do not hold for the period of growth and development.

If X, the frequency of stresses capable of killing, is substituted for N', the number of molecules having energies greater than that required for activation in the Maxwell-Boltzmann equation, and ΔH, the size of energy fluctuations just sufficient to kill (vitality), is substituted for E, the energy required for activation, then,

$$X = K'e^{\Delta H/RT}$$

where RT represents the average size of energy fluctuations, and K' is a constant. Since the death rate (R_m) is proportional to the frequency of stresses capable of killing (X), then

$$R_m = R_0 e^{at} = CX = CK'e^{-\Delta H/RT} = Ke^{-\Delta H/RT}$$

ΔH, the vitality, can be considered physiological efficiency. If we solve for this as a function of time, letting ΔH_0 represent vitality at time zero, then

$$\Delta H = \Delta H_0\left(1 - \frac{at}{\ln \frac{K}{R_0}}\right)$$

Since a, K, and R_0 are constants,

$$\frac{a}{\ln \frac{K}{R_0}} = B$$

where B is the linear decay constant of vitality, and

$$\Delta H = \Delta H_0(1 - Bt)$$

If the rate of loss of function (B) is calculated for an aging population, a close agreement is found between the curve obtained and that obtained by measurements of physiological function. In other words, this model predicts a linear decline in function.

Furthermore, the model predicts an inverse relationship between the log of the zero time mortality rate (R_0) and the slope of the Gompertz function (a). By calculating these variables for different societies with different environments and different stresses, an inverse relationship was found.

Exercises of this type do not lead to experiments that might provide information on mechanisms of aging at the cell or tissue level. Some of them also require assumptions that might be exceedingly difficult or impossible to justify. They do serve, however, to point out that the relationship between a linear decline in function and an exponential death rate need not be a mysterious one; that there are various ways in which the former could result in the latter.

Functional changes in some selected systems

A decline with age in function of the major organ systems responsible for maintaining homeostasis—the heart, blood vessels, kidney, and lung—is unequivocal. Every organ system in the body and every physiological process could be discussed in terms of aging. However, we shall restrict further discussion to certain systems that should be considered because of various arguments and hypotheses concerning basic mechanisms of aging, which will be presented in the next chapter. The systems to be considered are the central nervous system, the endocrine glands, and the system responsible for immune reactions.

One way of assessing function of the central nervous system is by psychological and behavioral testing, in accord with the notion that behavior is a product of neurones analogous to the production of bile by the liver. There is an enormous and very interesting literature on the psychology of aging. Most of this material would not be appropriate for inclusion here, since our primary concerns are with structural, chemical, and physiological alterations. However, some concepts from these studies can be summarized by noting that psychological reactions undergo the same types of changes with age that occur in the function of other organs; reactions become increasingly sluggish and inefficient. Psychomotor speed, learning ability, perception, and manipulative ability decline, while reaction times increase. Such declining function is also observed in the organs of special sense. There are, for example, increases with age in auditory reaction time and pupil latency period.

The role of age on the complex interrelationship between the central and autonomic nervous systems has been studied in terms of autonomic conditioning. A representative investigation was carried out with a group of young adults with a mean age of 20 years, and an old group, averaging 65 years of age. The subjects were exposed to a musical tone, and at the end of the tone were given electric shocks. The conditioned response measured over a series of trials was the extent of constriction of small blood vessels, an autonomic nervous system function. As shown in Fig. 6.18, the young subjects became very quickly conditioned, whereas the old group was almost entirely nonreactive.

Behavioral and conditioned reactions depend on a sequence of events beginning with a sensory perception and ending with a physiological response. For any alteration, a variety of interpretations regarding

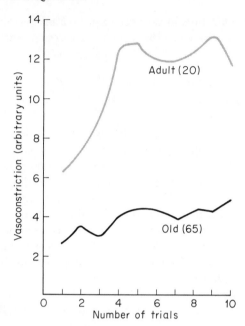

Fig. 6.18 Vasomotor conditioned responses for human males. Mean ages
in years are indicated. (Modified
from Shmavonian, et al. Ed. by Wel-
ford and Birren. 1965. Behavior,
Aging, and the Nervous System.
Charles C. Thomas Publ., Springfield,
Ill.)

causal mechanisms would be tenable, since neuronal, neurohumoral, permeability, vascular, and muscular factors are usually involved.

Changes with age in neurones, particularly in functional aspects, have not been studied in much detail. As mentioned in the previous chapter, there is some loss of human cortical neurones with age, but this is not generalized, there being no loss from the hypoglossal nucleus, for example. In short-lived laboratory mammals, cortical neurone loss has not been demonstrated. Lipofuscin pigment accumulation with age has been observed in neurones, but no attempts have been made to correlate the presence of this material with any functional property. Limited chemical analyses of brain lipids have not revealed age differences. In comparing protein synthesis in immature and old rat neurones, it was found that incorporation of a labeled amino acid occurred to a lesser degree in the old animals, but that turnover rates were similar in the two groups.

Regarding neuronal function, the conduction velocity of nerves in animals of different ages has received some attention. A preliminary study indicated that the fastest fibers of the sciatic nerve in 30-month-old rats conducted at a significantly slower velocity than those of 16-month-old animals. That this age difference may be due in part to extraneuronal factors is indicated by the finding that prior exercise of the animals caused a marked increase in the conduction velocity of the fastest fibers. In the 16-month-old rats, exercise increased conduction velocity from an average of 51 to 70 meters per second. In the old animals, conduction velocity increased from 20 to 45 meters per second because of exercise. Since neuromuscular activity appears capable of strongly influencing neuronal function, it is conceivable that part, at least, of the decline with age in reactivity of the nervous system is secondary to the general physiological decline associated with aging.

Neuromotor functional decline may be in part due to muscular weakness, as discussed in an earlier chapter. In addition, degenerative changes with increasing age have been described in preterminal nerve fibers and motor endplates. The number of nerve fibers innervating a muscle appears to remain constant.

Among the extraneuronal factors that would be expected to influence nervous system function is blood supply. Decreases in cerebral blood flow and oxygen consumption and a rise in cerebral vascular resistance with age have been observed. There is considerable scatter of values at each age, and carefully selected healthy old individuals give values for cerebral blood flow comparable to those in young adults. This relates to the problem alluded to earlier concerning the difficulty in dissociating arteriosclerosis, a disease which occurs in everyone, and which progresses at different rates in different individuals, from basic aging processes at the tissue level in all individuals. It would also be useful to know what the relationship of age to cerebral blood flow would be if the system were stressed in such a way that flow would increase to the maximum rate. Age differences in other physiological processes may not be demonstrated unless the system is stressed for maximum performance.

The declining function of the nervous system, which is undoubtedly of importance in the generalized aging syndrome, cannot be ascribed to intrinsic neuronal aging on the basis of current evidence. Although neuronal alterations could be responsible, many more systematic studies are required in order to determine the roles of activity of other systems, of vascular reactivity, and tissue permeability, and to determine whether primary cell changes precede or are correlated with age-related declines in neurone function.

Since the syndrome of aging is generalized throughout the mammalian body, attention has frequently been directed toward control or integrative systems; any age-related alteration might be expected to have widespread consequences. The endocrine glands, in particular, have a long history as a focal point in considerations of aging. These organs play key roles in growth, metabolism, homeostasis, and reaction to stress. They are of prime importance in bringing about sexual maturity. The endocrines would be likely suspects for a role in aging, and at various times it was believed that aging must be due to endocrine failure, and could be prevented by some type of endocrine therapy or gland replacement.

We would like to know if there are age-changes in the capacity of the endocrine glands to synthesize and secrete hormones, in the ability to deliver biologically active hormones to target cells in appropriate concentration, and in the ability of target cells to respond. Data of these types would be difficult to obtain, and in most cases inferences must be made from hormone concentrations in the blood, or from the urinary excretion of hormones or their degradation products. Such levels may vary with rates of degradation, excretion, and utilization, as well as with rates of synthesis and secretion. Hormone utilization and target organ reactivity might be influenced by vascular and permeability factors, or by the immediate past history of the animals in terms of generalized physiological activity.

Profound changes in the secretion of hormones have been observed early in development, and are associated with growth and the attainment of sexual maturity. These changes are not relevant to our discussion. After maturity there are declines in the production of sex hormones synthesized by the gonads. In females, the dropoff of estrogen production is associated with the disappearance of ovarian follicles, follicular cells being responsible for estrogen synthesis. There is similarly a decline in the secretion of 17 ketosteroids by the testes. There is apparently no age-related loss in interstitial cells of the testes, and it has been proposed that the endocrine dysfunction may be associated with a progressive peritubular fibrosis occurring with age. The decrease in gonadal steroid secretion is accompanied by increases in pituitary gonadotropin production. These are examples of organ aging. However, they are not of significance in the aging of animals, since the gonads are not necessary for life; removal of the gonads does not result in shortened life spans.

Sex hormones are also produced by the adrenal glands, and the amounts of circulating hormones would be functions of the activity of gonads and adrenals, plus possibly rates of degradation, utilization, and excretion. From determinations of urinary excretion it has been concluded that total estrogen levels in human males do not change significantly with age, but decline between about 40 and 60 years of age in the female and then remain quite constant. Androgens and 17 ketosteroids drop off logarithmically in both males and females.

The adrenal corticosteroids that are necessary for life appear less affected by age than the sex steroids. The levels of circulating and excreted corticosteroids do not vary significantly with increasing age in human beings. Old individuals appear capable of an adequate steroid secretion in response to stress. Similarly, the blood level of thyroid hormone, measured as protein-bound iodine, does not change with age.

Analyses of hormone concentrations in human pituitary glands have revealed no significant changes with age in adrenal- and thyroid-stimulating hormones or in growth hormone, and have shown age-related increases in follicle-stimulating and luteinizing hormones. The concentration of insulin in the human pancreas has not been found to change with age.

Regarding reactivity of target tissues, the administration of insulin is less effective in reducing blood glucose with increasing age. Diabetes is one of the diseases that shows an increasing incidence with age in a subgroup of the general population. A relationship between this disease and response to insulin has not been established.

The mobilization of lipids secondary to noradrenaline treatment does not vary with age, nor does the pressor response (vasopressin action) following injection of a hypertonic solution. When vasopressin is administered to rats, there is an increasing variability in the pressor response with age.

There have been many experiments in which old animals and human beings were treated with hormones in attempts to rejuvenate them. Some of these treatments have been beneficial in increasing performance—muscle strength, for example—or in stimulating a sense of well-being. However, such responses probably have little to do with aging, since many pharmacologic agents would be expected to have beneficial effects independent of the age of the subjects. Reports that aging has been inhibited or reversed in terms of life span, on careful examination, indicate that maximum life span has not been altered, but that the percentage survival curves become slightly more rectangular. This is most consistent with the view that old debilitated animals with diseases are kept alive a short while longer, in the same way that human beings dying of congestive heart failure may survive longer when treated with pressor agents; their heart failure is not caused by a deficiency in such agents.

We can conclude that there is no characteristic endocrine gland failure, with respect to the hormones necessary for life, which is associated with aging. The loss of tissue response to insulin treatment and the variability in response to vasopressin raise some interesting possibilities. If the reactivity of small blood vessels and control of passage of metabolites into cells become altered, many of the debilities of age could be explained. At the level of target organs, the amount of an agent delivered to cells would depend on small blood vessel density and reactivity and on permeability factors. The pressor response would depend on elastic properties of vessel walls as well as on metabolic reactions of smooth muscle cells; it has already been shown that peripheral resistance in small vessels increases with age. It would obviously be useful to know whether altered response to hormone action depends on intrinsic cellular changes, or on changes in the extracellular environment.

The complex series of reactions leading to antibody formation and function constitutes a unique type of system. In contrast to physiological processes, which work continuously to maintain a constant internal environment, immune mechanisms are called upon at irregular intervals to react to new or repetitive stimuli. The reactivity depends on the past history of the system in terms of antigenic stimulation, and on genetic factors. Aging processes may further influence reactivity.

In view of the different types of antigens, measurements, and species that have been employed in studying the relationship between age and immunity, it is not surprising that many findings are not consistent with each other.

As in so many of the systems we have considered, profound changes occur early in life in immune mechanisms. These deal with maturation of the immune mechanisms and with immune tolerance. We shall be concerned primarily with changes occurring after maturity.

The levels of naturally occurring antibodies decline with age. This holds for the isoagglutinins anti-A and B, and for antibodies against red cells of foreign species. If animals are immunized against a specific antigen early in life, there are progressive decreases over the life span in the percentage of animals with measurable antibody, and in the mean antibody titers of the responders.

When animals of different ages are injected with antigens, responses are variable. The antibody response to bovine serum albumin in rats and to horse serum in humans declines with age. In the case of *Salmonella* immunization, there is a decrease in the percentage of individuals who respond to the somatic antigen, but in those of the older groups who respond, the level of response is comparable to that of young individuals. No age-related decline in response to the flagellar antigen is observed. In mice the primary antibody response to flagellin does not change, but on secondary challenge, there is a marked decline in response as a function of age. In humans, no decline in the ability to respond to typhoid or Rh factor immunization has been demonstrated, and an enhanced response has been noted with age in response to an influenza vaccine.

Older animals give a diminished anaphylactic reaction. This has been shown with both guinea pigs and rabbits sensitized with horse serum. The number of animals dying of anaphylactic shock declines with age. The same phenomenon is noted when antibodies are passively transferred to animals of different ages, indicating that the difference in reactivity is not due to the ability to produce antibodies. The decreasing sensitivity to anaphylactic shock appears to be an exception to the previous generality that there is an increasing sensitivity to insults with age. This might be explained on the basis of a decreased ability of blood vessels and bronchioles to constrict, these reactions being required for anaphylaxis.

The most direct study of the effect of age on the ability of cells to produce circulating antibody has involved the injection of potential antibody-forming cells from spleens of animals of different ages into young irradiated animals. The injected cells then populate lymph nodes and spleens of the host animals, and their ability to produce antibody can be tested by treating the animals with antigen. As shown in Fig. 6.19, the antibody-forming ability per spleen rose to around

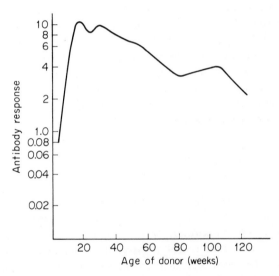

Fig. 6.19 Primary antibody-forming potential per mouse spleen as a function of age. (Redrawn from Makinodan and Peterson. 1966. Develop. Biol. 14:96.)

four months of age, and then decreased exponentially. Other studies indicated that this was not due to variations in the number of spleen cells, but that the percentage of cells which were incapable of responding decreased with age. It was also of interest that the antibody produced with increasing spleen age was predominantly of the 19S type, a type usually associated with early development.

With regard to fixed, or tissue, antibodies, the delayed type of hypersensitivity, manifested by skin reactions, drops off with age. This has been observed in the guinea pig reaction to poison ivy antigen, in human sensitivity to dinitrochlorobenzene, and in human food allergies. On the other hand, no differences between 3- and 18-month-old mice were observed in the ability to reject skin homografts.

In addition to the above changes in normal function of immune mechanisms, increasing age is associated with certain abnormalities in immune globulins and the appearance of abnormal antibodies in increasing percentages of the population. These alterations will be referred to again in the next chapter.

We can conclude that when antibody production is stimulated early in life, the level of antibody present falls progressively. This could be due to a loss of properly programmed cells in the course of cell turnover, or to losses of memory of individual cells by some intrinsic aging process. With regard to the ability of cells to respond to new antigens as a function of age, there are declines in the cases of some, possibly most, antigens, while responses to other antigens appear unaffected. It is possible that with the passage of time, more and more cells would be committed to the production of specific antibodies because of normal antigenic stimulation. The decreasing number of uncommitted cells might or might not be able to respond, depending on the type of antigen supplied. Degree of response might also depend to some extent on the relationship between the new antigens and antigens against which cells were already capable of making antibodies.

Growth and aging

Changes with age at molecular, cell, and tissue levels used to explain aging of an animal in terms of debilities, and death rates must also be capable of explaining, or at least be not incompatible with certain observations and correlations that characterize aging populations. One of the most significant observations in this category is a relationship between growth rate and rate of aging.

Animals which have a clearly defined life span are those which have a species specific size. These animals go through a period of growth, attain a size that is characteristic of the species, and grow no more. Furthermore, the debilities that we have been considering appear to begin, or at least to accelerate, at around the time at which this size is attained. This is particularly clear in the cases of death rates and physiological processes.

Animals that do not have characteristic sizes, or which continue to grow indefinitely have poorly defined life spans, or we are not able to say what their life spans are. A number of reptiles and fish grow in proportion to their food supply and continue to grow as long as they live. It would appear that they do age, and that the rate of aging is probably inversely proportional to their rate of growth, in that with increasing time they grow more slowly and perhaps age more rapidly, but we are unable to assign them characteristic life spans.

The relationship between growth and aging in mammals was brought out by experiments undertaken by McCay, a nutritionist, in the 1930's. McCay allowed his control rats to eat a well-balanced diet, rich in calories, at will. These animals grew rapidly until around 6 months of age and then gained weight more slowly until around 18 months, when their size and weights became stabilized. Experimental groups were given all essential nutrients, but they were starved for calories. They grew at very slow rates, so that at around 18 months of age they weighed approximately one-fourth as much as the controls. At various times, up to 1000 days of age, groups from among those starved for calories were put on the control diets. They rapidly gained weight, approaching that of the control group at the same age. The animals that grew slowly for a period beyond that over which rats normally grow, and which had periods of accelerated growth late in life, had greatly lengthened life spans.

Subsequent studies by McCay and others suggested that aging was truly inhibited by prolonging the growth period because the onset of diseases characteristic of aging was delayed in underfed animals. Lengthening of life span would also appear to be the result of continuing growth rather than small size of the animals, since keeping animals stunted at a constant size by dietary manipulation does not increase life span.

For any postulated mechanism of aging, an explanation of how the mechanism might be inhibited by growth processes would appear to be required.

Correlations among life span, body weight, brain weight, and metabolic rate

It is likely that different species of mammals age by similar mechanisms. Since there are great differences in life span among various kinds of animals, there must be factors characteristic of each kind of animal that determine rates at which aging processes proceed.

We can attempt to gain information on what these factors might be by considering what properties of different animal species are correlated with life span. Maximum life span is the most useful measure

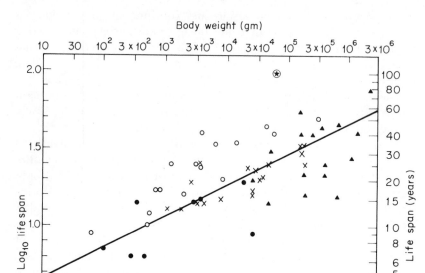

Fig. 6.20 Relation of life span to body weight for 63 species of mammals. ○— primates and lemurs, ●— rodents and insectivores, × —carnivores, ▲ — ungulates and elephants, ✷ — man. (From Sacher. 1959. The lifespan of animals. Ciba Found. Colloq. on Ageing, Vol. 5. J. & A. Churchill, London.)

of aging end points, since there are not enough data available for many families and genera of mammals for estimations of life expectancies and modal life span values.

There is a clear relationship between body size and life span (Fig. 6.20). The regression of log life span in years (x) on log body weight in grams (y) is

$$x = 0.198y + 0.471$$

and accounts for 60 percent of life span variance.

Brain weight is a better predictor of life span than body weight (Fig. 6.21) the regression of log life span on log body weight accounting for 70 percent of the life span variance. The significance of this is not clear, since brain weight follows body weight to a large extent,

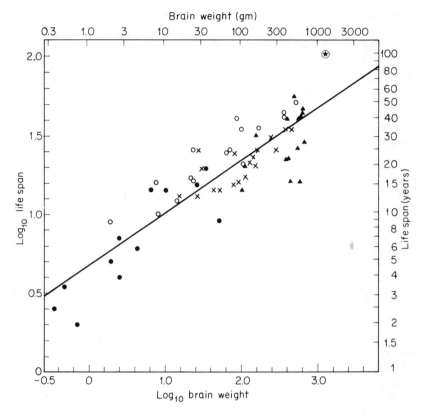

Fig. 6.21 Relation of life span to brain weight for species of animals. Symbols and source as in Fig. 6.20.

and other organs might be equal or better predictors of life span. It is possible, however, to calculate a brain quantity, the index of cephalization, which is a measure of brain development independent of body size. This quantity also correlates with life span, suggesting that some aspect of brain development per se influences rates of aging or probability of dying. It may be simply that smarter animals are better able to avoid being killed in one way or another.

Metabolic rates of animals of different species are also functions of body size. As animals become smaller, their metabolic rates increase. The smaller the animal, the larger the ratio of body surface to volume; heat loss would surpass heat production if metabolic reactions that produce energy did not increase with decreasing body size. The regression of log metabolic rate (m) on log body weight (y) is

$$m = -0.266y + 1.047$$

and the correlation coefficient is over 0.99. This means that we can substitute metabolic rate for body weight and obtain a relationship with life span as in Fig. 6.20, except that the plot would be a mirror image of the Fig. 6.20 data; the faster animals live, the shorter their life spans.

These correlations do not tell us anything about cause and effect. We have the choice of speculating that something about body or organ size, or about metabolic rate, influences rates of basic aging processes; or that additional unknown factors influence these dimensions and that the latter are independent of each other. We cannot ignore the fact that different kinds of animals age at different rates; attempts to explain how animal or organ size or metabolic rate might influence aging processes would appear to be justified.

Radiation-induced life-shortening

There is a zone of interaction between radiation biology and the study of aging that has given rise to a number of questions for both of these disciplines. When laboratory mammals were given doses of whole-body radiation early in life, it was observed that those which did not die of acute injury appeared to recover, but with the passage of time they lost hair, looked debilitated, demonstrated decreased activity, and died off at increasing rates, all of these changes occurring earlier than similar changes associated with natural aging. It thus appeared that irradiation accelerated the rate of aging or hastened the onset of aging processes.

Treatment of mice at 4 weeks of age with a single dose of whole-body radiation results in the types of percent survival curves shown in Fig. 6.22. The major effect of radiation is a displacement of curves to earlier ages. The amount of displacement is dose-related. This phenomenon has been studied in detail, and it has been found that the amount of life-shortening varies linearly with dose in certain strains.

Age at irradiation also influences life shortening. When the percentage shortening of remaining lifespan is calculated for mouse populations irradiated at different ages, data of Fig. 6.23 are obtained. This curve follows rather closely that for the role of age in sensitivity to acute radiation injury, determined by the amount of radiation required to kill 50% of a population. The data suggest that radiation life-shortening may occur by two mechanisms: one associated with growth of animals, and possibly depending on the number of dividing cells, and the second representing a nonspecific injury in aging animals, which become increasingly incapable of reacting to injuries of all types.

Survival curves for animals irradiated early in life suggest that radia-

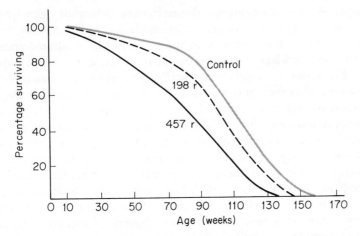

Fig. 6.22 Survival curves of mice irradiated with 457 r and 198 r at 4 weeks of age. (Redrawn from Lindop. 1965. Aging and Levels of Biological Organization. Univ. of Chicago Press, Chicago. © 1965 by the University of Chicago.)

Fig. 6.23 Amount of life-shortening caused by 100 r given at different ages in mice. (Redrawn from Lindop. 1965. Aging and Levels of Biological Organization. Univ. of Chicago Press, Chicago. © 1965 by the University of Chicago.)

tion hastens the onset of aging. However, any number of harmful treatments could cause animals to die off at earlier ages. A large number of studies have been undertaken to discover to what extent irradiated animals demonstrate an earlier appearance of normally occurring age-changes. If radiation simply hastened the onset of aging with all of its manifestations, diseases characteristic of aging should have earlier onsets, but their incidences should be unaffected. It has been shown that these diseases do appear earlier in irradiated animals, but that the incidences vary somewhat from those in control populations. Neoplasms of certain types, particularly leukemia, have increased incidences. However, incidences of these lesions depend on the age at which animals are irradiated; this may simply mean that the well-known carcinogenic effect of ionizing radiation is manifested in these animals, in addition to the life-shortening or age-simulating effect. Most importantly, life-shortening in irradiated animals is not due to a specific disease, or to diseases not seen in control animals; irradiated animals die from a variety of diseases associated with normal aging. This would indicate that radiation accelerates basic aging processes, or that aging processes and the consequences of radiation may act through some final common pathways.

Mammals contain an intrinsic, or physiological, clock that is of use in considering factors that alter life spans. This is collagen, which, as described in a previous chapter, becomes increasingly cross linked with age. The degree of cross linking can be used as a measure of biological age. Collagen is extremely resistant to radiation, and collagen present at the time of irradiation does not undergo accelerated cross linking. Thus, the effect of radiation is not a straightforward acceleration of biological aging.

In the case of radiation-induced life-shortening, as in natural aging, attention must be directed to the tissues in order to gain an appreciation of possible mechanisms. Because of the mutagenic effect of radiation, genetic damage would be a likely suspect. Very shortly after receiving a life-shortening dose of radiation, the liver cells of mice show large numbers of gross chromosomal aberrations—about two times as many aberrations as are found at the end of the normal life span. However, at the time of the greatest number of altered cells, the animals do not appear aged; apparent aging comes later. Also, the percentage of altered cells drops off with the passage of time, either by intracellular repair mechanisms or replacement of damaged cells. In other words, the number of liver cells with aberrations is not related to the apparent age of the animals. It is not known if this lack of correlation between altered chromosomes and life span holds for other organs. Offspring of irradiated animals age and die off at the same rates as control mice, indicating that genetic alterations affecting gametes are not responsible for life-shortening.

Histological examination of tissues of irradiated mice reveals the lesions and degenerative diseases of age. In addition, characteristic and widespread changes have been observed in the small blood vessels. Walls of arterioles and small arteries are thickened by the deposition of connective tissue elements, and fibrous connective tissue is laid down in and around the walls of capillaries. These changes have been referred to as arteriolocapillary fibrosis, or hyalinosis, and are shown in Fig. 6.24. Arteriolocapillary fibrosis may represent a low-grade inflam-

(a)   (b)   (c)

Fig. 6.24 Arteriolocapillary hyalinosis in mice 18 to 20 months after 600 rad whole-body irradiation. (a) Kidney, (b) spleen, (c) testis. (From Cottier. 1965. Aging and Levels of Biological Organization. Univ. of Chicago Press, Chicago. © 1965 by the University of Chicago.)

matory response to the injury of endothelial cells by the radiation. These changes may be of help in attempting to relate aging and late radiation effects at the tissue level.

The questions

We have now characterized aging mammals as animals which have certain progressive diseases, which show increasing incidences of other diseases, and which show increasing mortality from yet a third group of diseases and from injuries and insults of all types. Reactions to stress in these animals are diminished because of declining efficiency of all physiological processes and homeostatic mechanisms, and we have examined the role of age in some factors influencing physiological reactivity and homeostasis. Any aging processes at the tissue or molecular level postulated to be causes of animal aging must be capable of explaining these characteristic manifestations.

Furthermore, we have noted that growth inhibits aging, that different kinds of mammals age at different rates, and that low doses of ionizing radiation and age have similar consequences. Basic causes of aging must be related to, or capable of being influenced by, these phenomena. In other words, any postulated basic mechanism whose function is inconsistent with these observations is probably not an important cause of aging.

Some needed studies

1. Microphysiology. Information is required on changes with age in microvascular perfusion at various sites, permeability of tissue, diffusion of substances between vessels and cells, and elastic properties of small vessels and tissues. Since the most prominent changes with age might be in dynamic processes, in vivo studies in which systems are stressed for maximum performance would probably be most informative.

2. Neuromuscular function. As noted in the previous chapter, studies are required on functions of the long-lived fixed postmitotic neurones and muscle cells, and on their interrelationships. Data on age-changes in nerve conduction, motor end plate function in terms of acetylcholine production and degradation, and myofiber reactivity and contractability would be of great value. Ideally, experiments would be performed on neuromotor units isolated from their blood supply and environment, and obtained from animals which had exercised to the same extent.

3. Reactivity of target cells. Information on reactivity might be obtained by in vitro studies of the effects of such hormones as insulin and vasopressin on cells and tissues removed from animals of different ages. Again, the immediate past history of animals would have to be taken into account, and comparisons between animals which had had the same amount of activity would be most useful.

REFERENCES

Bellamy, D. 1967. Hormonal effects in relation to ageing in mammals. *In* H. W. Woolhouse [ed.] Aspects of the biology of ageing. Symposium of the Soc. for Exptl. Biol. XXI. Cambridge Univ. Press, Cambridge.

Casarett, G. W. 1964. Similarities and contrasts between radiation and time pathology. *In* B. L. Strehler [ed.] Advances in gerontological research, Vol. 1. Academic Press, New York.

Cohn, J. E. 1964. Age and the pulmonary diffusing capacity. *In* L. Cander and J. H. Moyer, [ed.] Aging of the lung. Grune & Stratton, New York.

Guttman, E., V. Hanzlíková, and B. Jakoubek. 1968. Changes in the neuromuscular system during old age. Exptl. Gerontol. 3:141.

Kohn, R. R. 1963. Human aging and disease. J. Chron. Dis. 16:5.

Legge, J. S. and C. M. Austin. 1968. Antigen localization and the immune response as a function of age. Aust. J. Exp. Biol. Med. Sci. 46:361.

McCay, C. M. 1952. Chemical aspects of ageing and the effect of diet upon ageing. *In* A. I. Lansing [ed.] Problems of aging. The Williams & Wilkins Co., Baltimore.

Ram, J. S. 1967. Aging and immunological phenomena—a review. J. Gerontol. 22:92.

Shock, N. W., R. Andres, M. Landowne, A. H. Norris, E. Simonson, and F. C. Swartz. 1964. Aging of the cardiovascular system. 2nd National Conference on Cardiovascular Disease, E. C. Andrus [ed.] Washington D.C.

Strehler, B. L. 1962. Time, cells and aging. Academic Press, New York. pp. 219–225.

Teller, M. N., G. Stohr, W. Curlett, M. L. Kubisek, and D. Curtis. 1964. Aging and cancerigenesis. I. Immunity to tumor and skin grafts. J. Nat. Cancer Inst. 33:649.

SEVEN

Aging of Animals:
Possible Mechanisms

The manifestations of age that we have considered are not very subtle. Aged animals are very different from mature ones. One might expect early agreement among students of aging on tissue changes that are most likely responsible for the aging syndrome and on the types of studies and experiments required for an understanding of cause-and-effect relationships. Such an agreement has not been the case; notions about causes of aging have generally followed the fashions of the times, and virtually every conceivable phenomenon has been proposed in the past, or is currently under consideration as a primary cause. It is extremely unlikely that the true cause or causes of aging have not been postulated and argued at one time or another.

Although basic mechanisms of aging are currently at the level of hypotheses or theories, any mechanism that is capable of explaining observations discussed in the previous chapter and is consistent with all established data should be worthy of serious consideration. Conversely, any tissue change or hypothesis that cannot be related to the manifestations of age or which is inconsistent with established information should be rejected as an explanation of aging.

The consequences of age are clear. Of the various causes that have been postulated, some are known to exist, while others have been argued on the basis that if they do occur, they would be reasonable explanations of aging. For example, latent viruses have been postulated as a cause of aging. It would first have to be shown that viruses become more widespread in tissues or become more active with age, and second, a reasonable explanation of how viral activity might cause the

148

debilities of age would have to be advanced. On the other hand, it is known that lipofuscin pigment accumulates in muscle cells and neurones with age. If one could explain debilities on the basis of this accumulation, lipofuscin would be a more reasonable cause than viruses.

A useful rule in scientific reasoning has been that if there are several ways in which a phenomenon might be explained, one should favor the mechanism that requires the fewest assumptions. In considering causes of aging, therefore, we should perhaps first attempt to rule out mechanisms that are known to exist rather than those which we assume or guess are operative. Also, we have observed that aging debilities occur throughout the mammalian body; we cannot ascribe consequences of age to a single organ. We might assume that the major manifestations of age result from one change or a small number of changes in a system that is common to all organs. Otherwise, we would have to make multiple assumptions about different types of alterations in the various systems and tissues, all proceeding at similar rates to cause debilities at different sites at about the same time.

Theories of aging deal with various levels of abstraction. It has been proposed that aging is due to tissue wear and tear, to random "hits" or mutations, or to the formation of free radicals, without specifying how these might cause debilities. Other theories are based on autoimmunity, on the accumulation of inert or harmful substances, and on cross linking of macromolecules.

Since the cause of aging must reside in chemical changes in cells or tissues, it would be profitable to direct our attention to what is known or what can be reasonably assumed about aging processes at these sites and their effects at higher levels of organization. It should be emphasized that although there are large gaps in our knowledge of basic processes, an enormous number of studies have been carried out, and we have a great deal of information, as indicated in earlier chapters. This information should at least permit the rejection of some hypotheses while favoring one or more of the others, and should indicate the types of studies required to support or negate likely possibilities.

Role of cells in animal aging

Most attempts to explain animal aging have, for obvious reasons, been based on cell alterations. It has been assumed that there must be widespread cell death or injury underlying the aging syndrome. Recent discoveries and concepts in biology have been applied to this assumption. It has been frequently postulated that aging is caused by alterations in the DNA code, or in transcription or translation.

A theory that aging is due to autoimmunity is based on abnormal serum globulins and autoantibodies found in increasing percentages of an aging population, and on some similarities between aged animals and animals with runt disease, a disease caused by antitissue antibodies. The view that aging is due to injury caused by free radicals arises from knowledge of how free radicals could alter cellular components, and from suggestive evidence that free radicals increase in the blood with increasing age.

There are several a priori considerations that weaken the view that cell loss is a cause of animal aging. If there were a random loss of cells throughout the body, even a very large number (one-third of the total cells, for example), individuals would simply be smaller by that amount. There is no obvious reason why this should lead to debilities. If cells at some sites remained relatively constant in number, while those in other organs decreased with age, the imbalance might then result in functional impairments. This would require a number of assumptions to explain selective cell loss and its consequences, which would not be justified on the basis of current information.

If aging were due to selective cell loss, the loss would have to be very great indeed, and some mechanism would have to appear that would interfere with cell replacement. The reserve of cells in organs is enormous; animals survive quite well with only 40 percent of a liver, part of one kidney, one lung, and with large areas of the brain destroyed. In order to cause decreased organ function, cell loss would have to reduce organ size to below these limits. In addition, regeneration would restore cell numbers in those organs where cell division can occur. No significant decrease in regenerative capacity with age has been demonstrated. Similarly, the short-lived fixed postmitotic cells appear to be replaced adequately in animals of all ages.

Most importantly, studies of aging tissues have not revealed cell losses after maturity that would begin to depreciate the known reserve. Some losses of cells occur, particularly in the nervous system of man, as discussed in Ch. 5, but these can only be described as trivial, in terms of losses required for functional impairment and the widespread debilities of age.

In summary, the view that the mammalian organism is a collection of cells analagous to a complex tissue culture and that aging is caused by the dying out of these cells is untenable.

If aging is not caused by the death and disappearance of cells, perhaps it is due to cell injuries or alterations. Some of the same problems in attempting to explain aging in terms of cell death are encountered in considering cell alterations, except that cells which remain viable but deficient in function may be more likely to result in debilities than cells which simply disappear.

Aging of cells and their components was discussed in Ch. 4 and 5. The short-lived fixed postmitotic cells, which clearly age, appear to do so independently of the animals that contain them; there is no evidence that these cells in an old individual are significantly different from those in younger animals. In other types of cell populations, no pattern of generalized loss of enzymatic activities or of ability to synthesize cell components is apparent. Occasional observations of decreases in these factors might depend on changes in cell environment or physiological state of the animals. It is of interest that while these life-maintaining factors in cells are unchanged, or show equivocal changes with age, organ function declines markedly and progressively. This would suggest that only components required for specialized function become altered, or that the declining function of organs does not depend on cellular changes.

There are not many ways in which cells could be permanently altered without killing them. Mutations, in particular, would be more likely to result in dead than altered cells. And effects of mutations, such as defects in the synthesis of specific proteins, have not been observed in cells of aging animals.

Observations underlying the somatic mutation theory of aging are, as described in Ch. 4, an increasing frequency of chromosomal aberrations in liver cells with age and a larger number of aberrations in short-lived, as compared to long-lived, mice. The mutagenic effect of radiation also serves to relate radiation life-shortening to an explanation of aging based on mutations.

There is no reason to believe, however, that the short-lived strain of mice undergo accelerated aging; such strains are known to have an increased susceptibility to certain diseases. Primary lung tumors, for example, develop in one-third to one-half of the animals in the short-lived strain used. Furthermore, there is no relationship between the actual number of aberrations and life span in the two groups, and aberrations do not increase significantly after growth cessation. More significantly, following radiation, the percentage of aberrations is about twice as high as that attained at the end of the life span, but rather than being dead, the irradiated animals survive, and the percentage of aberrations decreases. It is rather difficult to demonstrate an age-related decline in liver function, and liver failure per se is not a cause of death in old mammalian populations. This indicates that chromosomal aberrations in liver cells, which have been described in 80 percent of the cells under certain experimental conditions, do not cause functional impairment.

If such aberrations do not impair liver function at the instant they are present, there is no reason why similar changes should be damaging at other sites, regardless of differences in rate of cell replacement. In accord with this view, when the mutagen, nitrogen mustard, was administered in very high doses to mice for two-thirds of their life span, no life-shortening occurred. It must be concluded on the bases of these data that somatic mutations of the type that have been described cannot be a cause of aging.

Cell function may be impaired by the accumulation of substances. Lipofuscin accumulation occurs in neurones, and in cardiac and skeletal muscle. Other substances such as minerals may also accumulate, and may not have been discovered as yet because they are invisible by light microscopy. If the accumulation of substances such as lipofuscin interfered with nerve transmission, cardiac contractility, or reactivity of smooth muscle cells in blood vessels, many of the debilities of age could be explained. In a limited study, no correlation was found between the concentration of lipofuscin and cardiac function, but it could be argued that the heart may be able to compensate to a degree, and that there is considerable individual variation in this ability. An important role for the accumulation of lipofuscin and other substances has not been excluded.

Other possibilities for cell alteration are in the cell membranes and structural components such as myofilaments. These structures contain macromolecules, some of which are polymerized and rather inert metabolically. On the basis of what is known about chemical aging, we would suspect changes, in the nature of cross linking or the binding of small molecules. The aging of these structures has not been studied in any detail. Alterations in membranes might influence permeability of cells, while changes in structural proteins of muscle could hinder contractility. If either of these changes were widespread in the body, most of the declines in physiological function with age could be explained.

As noted earlier, the debilities of age cannot be accounted for on the basis of cell alteration or failure known to occur in any specific organ or system. Endocrine failure, long suspected to be a cause of aging, may be ruled out as playing a key role in the major manifestations of age. Although there is suggestive evidence that neurone function decreases with age, more studies are required to show that this is an intrinsic and irreversible cellular phenomenon, unrelated to cell environment and physiological state of the animal. The declines that have been demonstrated in the function of the immune system may mean that older animals have impaired reactivity to certain antigens, and may be more susceptible to some infectious diseases. It is also likely that increasing (though small) percentages of an aging population undergo tissue damages because of autoantibodies. However, in view of the characteristics of an aging population, described in the previous chapter, and the lack of tissue evidence of immune reactions, except in certain subgroups and certain inbred mouse strains, the notion that autoimmunity is a major cause of aging in natural populations is tenuous.

Some possibilities remain for a major role for cellular alterations in causing aging. It is also likely that certain types of cell changes will be found to result in some debilities in aging populations. We have been unable to build a strong case, however, for the major characteristics of aging animals being caused by the aging of their cells as it is presently understood.

Role of connective tissue in animal aging

Components of connective tissue and their changes with age have been described in Ch. 3. The most characteristic age-change is a progressive intermolecular cross linking of collagen. This is associated with decreases in concentrations of mucopolysaccharides at some sites. The discussion to follow will deal with collagen, although, in addition to the probable significance of changes in this molecule, collagen may serve as a model for similar alterations and consequences likely to be associated with reticulin, elastin, and structural proteins of basement membranes.

It was pointed out that collagen constitutes 25 to 30 percent of the total body protein, and is distributed in and around walls of all blood vessels, and around cells. Contraction and relaxation of muscle cells occur in a collagen-containing matrix, and the passage of materials between blood vessel and cell takes place through this type of tissue. Studies combining physical measurements and morphological observations indicate that collagen functions to maintain form and to limit deformations of tissues.

Progressive cross linking of collagen, which appears to occur throughout the body, would tend to interfere with the flexibility of fibrils, and thereby make tissues less mobile. Tissues might become more rocklike, a state incompatible with life.

Physiological impairment might occur at several levels. Cardiac muscle would be unable to contract efficiently, it having already been shown that the capacity of the heart to work drops off with age, and that heart muscle becomes more rigid. Large arteries would be less able to transmit contractile force, it being known that with increasing age these arteries become more like rigid tubes. At the level of capillaries and tissues, mobility would be damped. In the extracellular space, actual movement of substances might be hindered by excessively cross-linked structural proteins. Decreases with age in perfusion of organs and in tissue permeability, and increased peripheral vascular resistance were described in the previous chapter.

In adequate perfusion of tissues, impaired passage of materials between vessels and cells, and increasing stiffness of tissue per se form the bases of arguments relating debilities of age to cross linking of collagen. Since all physiological processes depend on tissue movement and diffusion of substances, the generalized physiological decline with age could be explained on these bases. An impaired passage of gases, nutrients, metabolites, hormones, antibodies, and accumulated toxins would, furthermore, explain why aging animals become increasingly susceptible to being killed by miscellaneous diseases, injuries, and insults.

If physiological decline with age is due to connective tissue alterations, this would explain why organ function in situ, kidney function, for example, declines markedly with age, while studies based on preparations in which vessel-connective tissue-cell relationships are destroyed show only equivocal changes, or none.

We cannot discuss here all of the specific diseases characteristic of aging in various mammalian populations. We can consider human populations, however, in terms of some diseases that are aging processes themselves. The complications of arteriosclerosis constitute by far the most common causes of death. The blood supply to inner layers of large blood vessels is limited even in young individuals, because small vessels from the outer layer do not penetrate very deeply. Decreased permeability and diminished perfusion with age could result in tissue ischemia, and in the trapping of lipids, glycoproteins, and minerals. Resultant inflammatory reactions would constitute the lesions of arteriosclerosis.

Hypertension would result from the increasing rigidity of large vessels and the increasing peripheral resistance.

Diseases such as arteriosclerosis and hypertension are complex; there are obviously predisposing and exacerbating factors. The above deals only with the specific role of macromolecular aging in pathogenesis.

The diseases that show increasing incidences with age are not aging processes themselves, and populations would age and die off even in their absence. One of these, malignant neoplasms, however, bears an interesting relationship to age, and kills off a sufficiently large segment of older populations to justify special consideration. One might speculate on roles of connective tissues changes in carcinogenesis, in terms of tissue hypoxia causing cells to become neoplastic, or aged connective tissue being more readily invaded by tumors, such invasion being necessary for the spread of a tumor. However, these notions require a large number of assumptions that go far beyond established information. Some other ways in viewing the role of age in neoplasia will be mentioned in a later section.

With regard to growth and aging, it will be recalled that newly synthesized collagen is soluble, and that it matures into insoluble collagen by the formation of intermolecular cross links. As long as an animal is growing, it will synthesize young, or soluble, collagen. Therefore, its collagen will continually be diluted by young collagen. The amount of young collagen will be proportional to growth rate rather than chronological age. Collagen as a whole will not be able to age until growth has stopped.

The inhibition of aging by growth would hold for any system in which aging is caused by reactions involving nonrenewable molecules. Growth processes would dilute any such population of molecules. One theory of aging that is inconsistent with the known effect of growth on aging is that of somatic mutations; growing animals should have more dividing cells, which would be more, rather than less, susceptible to mutations.

In the previous chapter it was pointed out that rate of aging correlates with metabolic rate and, negatively, with body and organ size.

It is possible that metabolic rate is governed in part by body size, and that rate of aging is influenced by metabolic rate. There are at least two ways in which cross linking of collagen could be accelerated by an increased metabolic rate. If an enzyme such as amine oxidase plays a role in the oxidative deamination of lysine leading to cross linking, a generalized increase in metabolism might cause increased concentrations of such enzymes. Alternatively, it has been shown that stresses exerted on collagen fibers in vitro cause the fibers to take on the physical properties of more densely cross-linked structures. Animals with higher metabolic rates would have higher frequencies of tissue stresses, which could result in more rapid cross linking of collagen.

The late effects of irradiation have been tentatively explained on the basis of widespread arteriolocapillary fibrosis, which has been shown to occur. Fibrosis at the capillary level would be expected to have effects on tissue mobility, perfusion, and permeability similar to those caused by increasing cross linking of collagen due to natural aging. Any new collagen forming secondary to irradiation would also become aged by cross linking. The fact that irradiation has more of an agelike effect, the younger the animals irradiated, may depend on more times being available for the collagen that is laid down in response to radiation injury to age itself by natural cross linking.

Other theories of aging are compatible with the correlation between metabolic rate and rate of aging, and with the radiation effect. Roles for free radicals, somatic mutations, and autoimmunity due to altered tissue antigens could be argued in terms of radiation and metabolic rate. As indicated earlier, however, either these theories are contradicted by other data, or not enough is known about their existence and possible consequences to construct a very plausible cause-and-effect sequence ending with the debilities of age.

A variety of chemical agents that interfere with the maturation of collagen and elastin have been discovered. The most thoroughly studied of these are certain nitriles, known as lathyrogens, and penicillamine. These have been given to rats and mice in attempts to inhibit aging—without success. Since the fibrous proteins of connective tissue are synthesized in response to stress and in amounts appropriate to the degree and type of stress, tissues probably compensate for a partial defect in maturation by the synthesis of greater amounts of collagen and elastin. Any agent given in sufficient concentration to cause a permanent decrease in absolute amounts of insoluble protein would be too toxic. Since that cross linking of collagen which is an aging phenomenon occurs in mature, insoluble collagen, it might be possible eventually to find an agent that will maintain the collagen in its optimal mature state by inhibiting the formation of additional cross links. An undertaking of this type would provide important evidence for or against the view that cross linking of collagen causes animal aging, as well as possibly demonstrating the feasibility of inhibiting mammalian aging.

The speculative nature of the foregoing discussion is obvious. The value of the collagen cross linking theory of aging lies in its starting with established information on aging of collagen, proceeding to impaired function of all organs by making use of additional known facts, and its being capable of explaining major debilities. It also satisfies the criteria of being compatible with relationships between radiation, growth, and metabolic rates, and aging. Since it is this theory that is best able to explain aging in terms of current information, perhaps it should receive the highest priority for future investigations.

The view that collagen cross linking causes aging is a variation of one of the oldest theories of aging—that the latter is caused by syneresis of body colloids. This view also supports the cliché that a man is as old as his arteries, and suggests that when Leonardo DaVinci claimed that aging was due to thickening of tunics of veins which restricted the passage of blood, he may not have been very wrong.

Age and neoplasia

There is a clear relationship between age and the incidence of tumors in mammalian populations, in that different types of tumors appear on schedule, and that ages of maximum incidence are different for different kinds of malignancies. The possible role of host factors in controlling viability, growth, invasion, and spread of tumors has been mentioned previously. Future studies may show that some components of the physiological decline with age, having to do with permeability, vascular reactivity, or immunological reactions, permit the growth and spread of tumors. Since incidence appears to be the major age-related phenomenon, however, some theoretical aspects of time and the malignant transformation of cells will be considered.

In order for a cell to be malignant it must have a certain small number of properties. One would be some alteration in rate of cell division or destruction so that the number of cells increases. The cells have to be able to invade, to separate from one another in order to metastasize. And they must in some way avoid controls on growth and function exerted by other tissues. The number of properties we select is arbitrary, but the number required is probably small—four would be convenient for consideration. Some of these properties are shared with certain normal cells; many cell populations can increase in number, for example; leukocytes normally spread throughout the body, and both leukocytes and trophoblast tissue have invasive ability. Also, benign tumors would have some of these properties not present in the cell of origin. Each cancer cell, however, would require all of these abilities.

In order for a cell to have all of these properties, it must be subjected to events or "hits" that bring about alterations. Hits could be mutations, viral infections, or any other events whose consequences would be transmitted to subsequent generations.

Of course, a specific number of hits could be required for the alteration of a single biological property. Or a sequence of events might be necessary for the accumulation or depletion of some component, or for the expression of viral activity.

Age becomes an important factor, because time would be required for a given number of hits to occur in a cell. By use of probability theory, times required for a certain number of hits per cell, or the probability of a certain number of hits as a function of time can be calculated. However, such calculations assume that the frequency of mutation or similar change is constant with time, that the probability of hits or successes remains constant, and that the probability of a hit is independent of the number of previous hits. Since some of these assumptions may not be true, it will be just as useful for our purposes to assume only that more time is required for more hits per cell.

Starting with a large population at birth, we know from human and laboratory animal data that with the passage of time certain segments of the population will die off with characteristic types of malig-

nancies. An idealized view of this pattern is shown in Fig. 7.1, where
A represents tumors of early development; *B,* malignancies characteristic of growth and maturation; and *C, D,* and *E,* tumors of the aging
population.

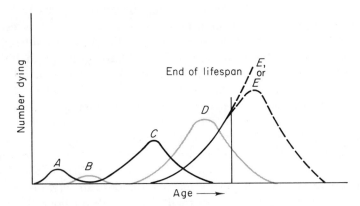

Fig. 7.1   Deaths of subgroups of a population from different kinds of neoplasms as a function of age.

Two questions arise: Why do some tumors appear earlier than
others? Why does the incidence of all tumors not increase with age
regardless of age at onset? Age of maximum incidence could depend
on the number of additional hits required by certain cell types in
order to have the required four. For example, tumors of young animals could be of a cell type in which only two hits are required because the cell normally has properties equivalent to the other two
hits. Or the susceptible subgroup could be born with a genetic predisposition—that is, could be born with one or more hits. In order for
the incidence not to rise indefinitely with age, the probability of
getting new hits of the inborn type would have to be very low when
compared to the probability of getting postnatal hits.

The appearance of different malignancies as the population ages
could be due to the number of postnatal hits required for different
tumors. For example, the cells of cancer *C* may have had two hits to
start with, and require two more; cancer *D* may originate from cells
that already had one hit and required three more; *E* may require all
four hits, and show an increasing incidence at the time the whole
population dies off.

The frequency of hits for certain types of tumors could also increase
with age in subgroups because of special types of risks. Cigarette
smoking might provide a hit in the population of heavy smokers, for
example.

In addition to a priori considerations, evidence for the accumulation of hits is found in carcinogenic effects of mutagens and viruses, and in the development of malignancies in benign tumors and premalignant lesions. Cancers are more likely to develop in these lesions than in tissues of origin, possibly because such lesions already have some of the required hits.

Descending limbs of the curves in Fig. 7.1 are most readily explained in terms of the suspectible group for each type of tumor dying out while the resistant segment of the population survives. This would be the case if the susceptible population had a genetic predisposition or inborn hits, and if the probability of hits of this type's affecting the general population were very low. A susceptible group might also be one exposed to certain hazards; cigarette smokers, radiologists, and uranium mine workers would be candidates for more hits than would the general population. Members of a group may be more susceptible to sustaining a permanent hit than the general population. The entire population may be exposed to a virus, for example, but while one group becomes infected—that is, sustains a hit—the remaining population may halt the infection, become immune, and not have a future risk of that type of hit.

These concepts indicate the need for a search for evidence of hits before final malignant transformation. This would be most feasible in certain mouse strains. Over 90 percent of the animals in strain AKR develop lymphatic leukemia on schedule, starting at 6 to 8 months of age. Comparative studies of lymphocytes in weanling animals of this strain and of a strain that does not develop leukemia might demonstrate early hits in the AKR cells.

REFERENCES

Blumenthal, H. T. and A. W. Barns. 1964. Autoimmunity and aging. Adv. in Gerontol. Res. 1:289.

Harman, D. 1965. The free radical theory of aging: effect of age on serum copper levels. J. Gerontol. 20:151.

Kohn, R. R. 1966. A possible final common pathway for natural ageing and radiation induced life-shortening. *In* P. J. Lindop and G. A. Sacher [ed.] Radiation & ageing. Taylor & Francis, Ltd., London.

Walford, R. L. 1967. The general immunology of aging. Adv. in Gerontol. Res. 2:159.

Welch, J. P. 1967. Somatic mutations and the aging process. Adv. in Gerontol. Res. 2:1.

EIGHT

Evolution and

Programming of Aging

In the systems in which aging can be most readily observed—macro-molecules, short-lived fixed postmitotic cells, and animals—changes are clearly programmed, in that they can be predicted with considerable precision. One might assume that the program resides in genes. How-ever, this view is insufficient, because it does not provide insight into mechanisms at higher levels, and molecules and structures are likely to participate in reactions not intended by genes.

Evolution may be related to aging in several different ways. Age-changes could be the necessary consequences of some useful property or function that was selected for; in order for a molecule or cell to carry out a necessary function, it must be constructed in such a way that age-changes are unavoidable. Aging processes could be selected for on the basis of some benefit to the organisms or species. Age-changes could be essentially accidental—unrelated to any function, and occur-ring because no mechanism has evolved to prevent them.

At the level of macromolecules, there is every reason to believe that the program is the molecular structure, and that, at least in some cases, aging is the unavoidable consequence of development required for specific function. The function of collagen requires the formation of strong fibers and fibrils. Therefore, collagen molecules are pro-grammed to aggregate and undergo cross linking. This cross linking does not stop at maturity of the fibrils, however, but continues and is responsible for collagen aging. Apparently no mechanism has evolved to prevent this excessive cross linking or cause significant turnover of

160

mature collagen. Aging of collagen might be viewed as both an unavoidable consequence of a necessary trait, and a continuation of developmental processes.

Other macromolecular reactions such as the accumulation of lipofuscin might, again, depend on programs built into the molecular structure, but be accidental in terms of any function. Accumulation could then occur if no mechanism were available for removal of aggregates.

Organelles and enzyme molecules that have regular turnover rates may deteriorate by denaturation or reactions of other types mentioned in Ch. 2 and 4. Since function depends on structural integrity, mechanisms for destruction and replacement of altered molecules and organelles would have to have evolved very early.

Reasonable explanations for the deterioration of short-lived fixed postmitotic cells are that their specialized functions utilize so many of the cell's resources that vegetative processes cannot be maintained, or that cells are killed as a result of some specialized reactions. In such cases, aging would be an unavoidable by-product of properties that were selected for. Again, this would necessitate the early evolution of mechanisms for the removal and replacement of altered and dead cells.

Degeneration and death of cells in development appear necessary in most cases for organogenesis. Such aging processes must have been selected for in some way. Either specific lethal reactions might be selected for, or mechanisms for protecting or replacing these cells could have been selected against.

The role of evolution in aging of animals has been the subject of considerable speculation. Selection for a trait can be most readily explained if the trait gives a reproductive advantage and has survival value during the reproductive period. It is more difficult to explain how some trait that is manifested in the postreproductive period could be selected for. Animals with such a trait would not tend to leave any more descendents than animals without the trait. It has been suggested that in some social animals, old, nonreproducing animals compete with younger animals for food, and thereby hinder reproduction of the young. Therefore, if some genetic trait appeared which caused animals to die as their reproductive capacity declined or ceased, this would be selected for. On this basis it has been suggested that early in evolution of a species, animals were essentially immortal or had indefinite life spans, and that aging was brought about by selection for shorter life spans.

Although selection for aging processes may occur in some species, there are more plausible explanations for mammalian aging based on the relationship between growth and aging, and on selection for longer life spans operating during the reproductive period. It was pointed out in the previous chapter that animals which show the most clearly programmed aging are those which have a species specific size. Having a specific size is probably of great adaptive value for various animals in different ecological niches. This would lead to the selection of factors that cause growth cessation. Molecules and structures that are metabolically inert would then not be diluted or turned over by growth, but would persist and age.

Few animals in the wild have the opportunity to age and die of degenerative processes. Early in the evolution of a species it is likely that animals were killed off by many different types of diseases, both intrinsic and environmental, very early in life. There would be great selection pressure for the development of defenses against these diseases during the reproductive period. This would result in a progressively longer life span until reproductive capacity declined markedly or was exhausted. Selection would also occur over the period in which young offspring must be cared for. After this period there would be no mechanism by which defenses or life-lengthening processes could be selected for, other than by the unlikely successful competition of old against young. Nonreproducing animals or those with very diminished reproductive capacity would then be left with some uninhibited lethal processes or susceptibilities.

In terms of one theory of aging—that based on the cross linking of collagen—in the nongrowing, nonreproducing animal, there would be no pressure for the evolution of mechanisms that would cause collagen to turn over, or inhibit cross linking. Aging of animals would be the unavoidable consequence of molecular aging.

According to the above views, the evolutionary origins of aging are in processes that restrict growth and in duration of the reproductive period. The latter depends primarily on gonadal function. Aging processes in gonads, particularly depletion of ova, are probably of major importance in determining when more generalized aging begins or accelerates.

To return to the question of genes and the inheritance of aging processes, aging is, of course, inherited in the sense that genes determine whether an animal will be a rat or a man, and a rat ages faster than a man. It is more useful to ask if studies of gene action will provide insight into mechanisms causing aging of animals. On the basis of current information it would appear that such studies might tell us why or how aging processes are initiated, but would not indicate which processes occur subsequently, or important details of their progression.

REFERENCES

Strehler, B. L. 1962. Time, cells, and aging. Academic Press Inc., New York. Pp. 219–225.

NINE

Some Judgments About

the Study of Aging

We have seen from the various levels at which aging processes occur that these processes constitute a major area of biology. In fact, they deal with the added parameter of time for most living systems. Furthermore, they underlie the most important public health problems in modern societies. It is inevitable that aging will receive increasing attention in biomedical research. In the case of intact animals, there are no reasons why aging processes will not be completely understood eventually, and methods devised for their inhibition.

Progress in the formulation and acceptance of concepts has been slow. This is not due to lack of data, but is the result of difficulties inherent in the field. It is frequently difficult to know what basic system to study or what types of studies to undertake to answer questions about alterations occurring at higher levels of organization. Aging processes are easily defined in the abstract, but it may be difficult to identify a process under observation as an aging one, and to distinguish it from a disease in a certain subgroup. An aging population is changing in many ways, and conclusions may be based on statistical artifacts. Distinguishing causes from effects is a common problem, and when several different causes might have a certain effect, there is often disagreement on the cause most likely to be the true one. In addition, a great deal of confusion has arisen because of the temptation to generalize from an observation in one type of animal or system.

The view that aging is aging and that one can study any system and generalize to all systems is clearly not tenable. If a question is asked about aging of the entire animal, there would be little justification for studying intermitotic cells in detail unless preliminary studies showed that changes in these cells were associated with significant changes in function of the animal. Similarly, the liver would probably be a poor choice for an organ to study in regard to animal aging because it does not appear to be a major contributor to the debilities of age, presumably because of its enormous cell reserve and regenerative capacity. On the other hand, if the question were about cell aging, it would be more reasonable to study fixed postmitotic cells than turning-over cells, or organ function where extracellular factors may be important.

The type of animal chosen for the study of animal aging should, again, depend on the specific question being asked. Coelenterates consist largely of turning-over cells, and at least some species may be immortal. Insects and rotifers are composed of fixed postmitotic cells, while mammals contain all types of cells, large amounts of extracellular substances, and a complex cardiovascular system. There is little reason to believe that such animals with very distant phylogenetic relationships and very different types of architecture age by similar mechanisms.

If life span is used as a measure of aging, it is essential that something be known about mechanisms of death. Mayflies might seem to be convenient for the study of aging, since adults live only a day or so. Death, however, is due to starvation because mouth parts are atrophied. The mouse as a species has a mean life expectancy of around 24 months. If a mouse population under observation has a mean life span of 16 months, deaths are almost certainly due to a specific disease and not to aging processes, as usually defined. Any changes in life span of such a population due to experimental manipulations would be of uncertain significance. Similarly, since life-shortening can be caused by any number of treatments, it should not be accepted as accelerated aging unless it can be shown that physiological decline and mechanisms of death follow the same patterns as those in the naturally aging population. On the other hand, experimental lengthening of life span beyond that recognized as maximum for the species would be likely to represent inhibition of aging.

A major problem inherent in the study of aging animals is that there can be no really satisfactory controls—that is, animals existing in time without aging. Longitudinal studies in which the same animals are studied over their life spans would be more meaningful than studies based on sampling of animals of different ages. Also, as a population ages, a continual selection occurs as members are removed by death. This can give very misleading data. For example, if some harmful substance or a by-product of some harmful reaction accumulates with age, and if animals die when this reaches a high level, studies of populations of different ages may indicate that the concentration of this substance remains constant with age, or actually appears to decrease in old animals.

Other misleading data could result from not taking into account differences between development and aging. A system may change in a rat between birth and 10 months of age, and remain rather constant thereafter, representing an aspect of maturation. If 3- and 18-month-old animals are studied, conspicuous differences would be observed, and might be assumed to represent an aging process. However, the same differences would be observed in 3- and 10-month-old animals, and little change might be detected between 12 and 30 months.

The problem frequently arises of trying to decide which, if any, change known to occur at the molecular or tissue level is responsible for a given debility. It may be practically impossible to devise a study that would prove any cause-and-effect relationship. A first step might be to ascertain which of the basic changes are truly aging processes in terms of universality within the population, irreversibility, and progression. Use can then be made of postulates analagous to those of Koch relating bacteria to disease: Is the basic change always present when the debility is present and does it always precede the debility? Is the debility always present when the basic change is present? Is there a positive correlation between extent of the two? The basic change that best satisfies such postulates should be favored as a cause of a given debility.

Difficulties in the study of aging make investigations in this area particularly challenging. Aging processes constitute exceedingly important problems, both in basic biology and disease. Application of the highest talents and major resources to their solution is required, and would be fully justified.

Index